INVI
SCHEMES

Invisible Schemes
By John McGlade

© John McGlade

ISBN: 9781912092055

First published in 2022

Published by Palavro, an imprint of
the Arkbound Foundation (Publishers)

Cover artwork and design:
John McGowan and Sorepaw Productions

Arkbound is a social enterprise that aims to promote social inclusion, community development and artistic talent. It sponsors publications by disadvantaged authors and covers issues that engage wider social concerns. Arkbound fully embraces sustainability and environmental protection. It endeavours to use material that is renewable, recyclable or sourced from sustainable forest.

Arkbound
Rogart Street Campus
4 Rogart Street
Glasgow, G40 2AA

www.arkbound.com

INVISIBLE SCHEMES

JOHN MCGLADE

palavro

PUBLISHING

To Dad, Mum and Paul.

schēm | **e** (sk-) *n.* & v. **1.** *n.* a systematic arrangement. **2.** *n.* artful or underhand design. **3.** *v. i.* make plans, esp. in underhand or secretive way. **4.** (*Scots*) *n.* a local authority housing estate.

Contents

1

McCann doesn't necessarily believe everything Marky Boy tells him when he describes the schemes he's been to, but he studies him closely and listens carefully.

Every self-made man wonders at some point what he has achieved, and asks himself: was it worth the effort? The scheming and cajoling, the bribing and stabbing, can all seem like a game played out for the amusement of some unseen spectator.

When the firm goes global, your friends could be anywhere – so could your enemies. When contacts disappear, allies turn, networks collapse, and deals evaporate, even the most assured businessman might look at himself and wonder what lies within.

Such a man, who only ever shone his light to find weaknesses in others, might wince under the spotlight of self-examination. In a ruined industrial unit on the edge of the city, McCann squeezes a chewed rubber bone in his hand; pigeons slap themselves daft in the rafters. There's a puddle on the concrete floor; its scummy surface seethes with the thrashing tails of tiny black tadpoles.

He knows corruption has laid its red lines straight to his heart. It is only these words, lighter than air, rushing towards him from between Marky Boy's thin blue lips, that offer a tenuous thread by which he might escape.

Schemes of Bureaucracy (1)

[——] is a scheme of renewal.

The main square was packed for its official opening; children danced, dignitaries spoke, and ribbons were cut.

While the gala was in full swing, at the back of the scheme a column of vans, trucks, and lorries slipped in unnoticed. By the time the locals returned home, the invaders had scattered poles, tarpaulin, and machinery everywhere.

A swarm of scaffolders caged every building. Even as the joints were being tightened, squads of workies scrambled up and laid out their tools. They bawled up and down at each other from their perches as white-shirted men with clipboards shouted from the pavement. At the end of the day, banners were unfurled from the top of each scaffold, which fell open to reveal perfect life-sized images of the buildings underneath.

Then the real work got underway. Every morning, more workers poured into the scheme, only to disappear behind the tarpaulin. The clipboard men were too busy to discuss the work, but did say the council regretted any inconvenience. When pressed, they hoped it would be finished sooner rather than later.

It emerged that every house in the scheme, now hidden beneath its own likeness, was being searched for early signs of decay. Each brick was scrutinised and every inch of grouting fingered to check for poor construction and substandard materials. Behind the tarpaulin, men prodded, scraped, and tapped; they banged, clattered, and crashed, while the residents tiptoed around them.

The work continues today. The scheme's mask still hangs over its face, tatty and frayed, a faded reminder of the day it was born. When asked about their slow progress, white-collared men with smartphones say the work is now entering a key phase. When pressed, they hope it will be over sooner rather than later. But behind its sagging portraits, [——] is a scheme of perpetual renewal, so the work can never be finished.

The residents would love to have a peek at the homes in which they live, to see them as they really are, and perhaps steal a glimpse of life as it might be, were they only left to get on with it. It's rumoured that decades of non-stop buffing-up has kept the houses in rude health, that they look even better than they did when they were built. Others say that, under their masks, the houses have been stripped back so severely they are pitiful, skeletal ghosts of the homes they once were. But the pictures on the banners never change, so no-one really knows.

Walking through [——] today, it's hard to find a resident among its vast army of occupation. Each day before dawn, columns of vans snake in nose to nose; mobile shops and burger stalls pitch up to service the taskforce, while in the central square, between the portacabins, hard hats muster.

Schemes of Aesthetics (1)

[——] is a scheme of flickering lights.

Older residents recall casual strolls at dusk beneath elegantly tapered stone lampposts – their long, gracefully arced necks nodding a polite 'Good evening' to passers-by. Back then, you could amble through the streets at ease, warmed by the inner glow that comes of being watched over: the lamps, golden baubles in a black, winter sky, would chart a safe way home.

The lampposts' fine design, exquisite proportion, and delicate detail made for a nightly guard of honour, a dignified tribute to civility.

But walk those streets today and you'll find, where gentility once stood, ranks of utilitarian metal poles in battleship grey, permanently at attention.

At night, they glare down on the scheme, arms held at stiff right angles as if to mock the curving backs of its pensioners, the slouching shoulders of its youth. Each pole hurls a hard white disc onto the pavement, as though in anger at being forced to carry out its spiteful vigil. Darkness pools between the lamps, so passing eyes must adjust to the light's ever-changing intensity. The harsh beams dazzle, accuse, and disorientate, so that walking at night feels like being dragged through a series of interrogations.

As the sun falls behind [——]'s tenement roofs, curfew begins: the scheme blinks, buzzes, and hisses, and its dreadful nightwatchmen flicker to life. At their feet, purple ducting erupts, fracturing the tarmac, tripping the unwary. Years of imperfectly patched electrical faults cause the new LED lamps to wink on and off in complex sequences, a disturbing light show that might herald the appearance of a demon.

The original lampposts are all gone but, outside one house, there's an arch made from the upper parts of two that were pulled from a skip. They lean on each other like a pair of blind, broken hobby horses whispering their last confidences, martyrs on the gate, a warning to all who walk here: darkness has reclaimed the streets.

Schemes of Coercion (1)

[——] is a scheme of momentum.

Soon after arriving, you'll encounter the Ball. It might drop behind you from a rooftop or ledge, or maybe roll along the top of a fence before falling to street level in front of your face.

Your first sighting of it could be through a gap between two tenement blocks; it might be running past the lift doors in the high flats as they open onto the eighteenth floor; or you'll take a blind corner in a narrow back lane and find it dead ahead – coming right at you.

There's no need to panic, it's nothing personal. All that's required at the critical moment is that you stand aside, stay still, and let the Ball pass unhindered.

It's black, six feet in diameter, and perfectly smooth although, as it grazes your nose, you might notice a seam dividing it into two hemispheres. What is it made of? Is it solid or hollow? What drives it on? When did it start? Will it ever stop? These questions have been asked over and over by local people down the years, but none have been answered.

Meanwhile, the Ball trundles along pavements, rumbles through gutters, bounces over speed bumps: the scheme is an endless groove carrying the Ball around a closed loop. Its presence has given rise to a social convention that is followed by everyone. Whether the Ball moves past the busy main gate of a primary school, crosses the road in front of a bus, or ploughs through a football pitch in the middle of a match, activity is immediately suspended to ensure the Ball rolls on unhindered; time slows to a stop around the Ball as it would near a black hole.

If you stay a while, you'll realise the Ball exerts a retarding force on every aspect of life: the papergirl, arm in her satchel, halts at a gate; two women chatting on the shopping parade are forced apart and lose their thread; an old man heading for the bookies drops his stick as he stumbles onto railings.

Each day, everyone in the scheme encounters the Ball at least once. The interruptions seem trivial, lasting only a few seconds, never intrusive enough to drive anyone to drastic action such as attacking the Ball or standing in its way. But measured over the long term, each person suffers incalculable loss: a life with inbuilt disturbance, intrusion, and hesitation can never run true. In [——], all forward momentum resides in the Ball, whereas people constantly check their stride, rethink their intentions, lower their targets, and abandon their goals.

In the middle of the night, there's thunder on the slates. As it rolls overhead, it terrifies children and forces lovers to separate: the Ball never sleeps.

[——] is a scheme of numbers.

Stacks of bricks block the pavements, and piles of rubble shut off open ground. Fluttering tape marks out new foundations alongside mangled iron rods that sprout like weeds from beds of pulverised concrete; slithers of smashed slate line the gutters, and scaffolding jabs out at every corner.

The scheme has always been in transition. A carousel of environmental, regulatory, and architectural snags haul down its houses, and throw up new ones in their place, which are then torn down when the next problem arises: weak foundations, misunderstood instructions, illegal building materials, new safety concerns. The displaced residents live like pinballs, fired from one end of the scheme to the other and back again.

As a result, addresses flit in and out of existence. Where tenements are built, perhaps six or eight flats to a close, the close numbers rise accordingly, leaping in sixes or eights, whereas the street might previously have had terraced rows, numbered in twos. And when the tenements give way to multi-storeys, the numbering will again change. In time, each street reuses all the available numbers, over and over. Today, on one road, a maisonette stands at 313. A few years ago, 313 was the upper left corner of a four-in-a-block. Before the scheme arrived, a mile separated 311 and 313, two isolated farmhouses

Confusion arises about which addresses currently exist, so postal deliveries are unpredictable. Letters and packages can turn up years late, after lying in the sorting office until a defunct street number is re-activated. Most deliveries are made to the correct address, but the wrong house, to someone living an entirely different life to the person named on the envelope.

Everyone here knows that to return to sender would only cause more confusion, because the forwarding address is likely also to be inhabited by someone unconnected with the letter. So whenever delayed mail turns up, people just deal with it as best they can, treating it as they would their own.

Letters from banks, lawyers, and insurance companies regarding long-lapsed accounts, cases, and policies are answered promptly, and in as much detail as possible. Old debts are paid off without comment; financial windfalls are accepted in the same spirit; personal messages are given the appropriate emotional response – sympathy for the writer's losses, or heartfelt delight at their success; love letters from strangers are read with longing and joy.

As walls rise up and roofs come crashing down, only the numbers hold their place – at the still point between creation and destruction.

Schemes of Abandonment (1)

[——] is a scheme of blank walls.

Whooshing nozzles herald the dawn; wielded by figures in white hazmat suits, chemical jets scour, exfoliate, and rinse the scheme's surfaces, removing every trace of graffiti.

As the bulky figures drive off in their vans, drowsy residents rise and peer out at bus shelters, bins, buildings, and lampposts free from the scourge of scrawls and scribbles. The scheme's walls bear no obscenity, insolence, aggression, tribalism, or alienation, but instead symbolise that trancelike, untroubled state of mind that exists beyond words, thoughts, and causes.

Blank, too, are the minds of the waking residents, because no-one ever remembers their dreams. They're erased by the jets' abrasive white noise, although sometimes vague impressions of the previous night's visions linger: hunched forms, silhouettes arrayed like ciphered characters forming an incomprehensible footnote to the night sky.

But these vanish with the new day's turning of the page, on which each person spells out their existence in their actions, until the chapter ends with closed curtains and drawn blinds.

Then another story unfolds: black clad figures spill out of lanes, ducking the horizon as they cross open ground. Under ski masks and hoodies, they gather in back courts and bus shelters, around bins and lampposts. They size up windowsills, doors, angled roofs, and midden walls; they crouch under classroom windows; clamber over shops; tiptoe behind the old folks' home; swarm over garages and sheds. Armed with spray cans, magic markers, tins of paint, brushes, and biros, they script the night.

Some do it to reach out to readers; others just say what they feel must be said. But each understands that to cover something in words is ultimately an act of love. As the scheme sleeps, it becomes a tangled ball of string; a nest of spiders; an anarchic jumble of tags, menshies, shout-outs, slogans, allegiances, flourishes, IDs, declarations, threats, questions, cartoons, self-portraits, and swirling, fleeting impressions plucked from the dark. These tumble into the residents' dreams, merging the everyday with the improbable, the possible with the unthinkable, until the roar that heralds the morning's ablutions banishes the ravings of night, and the sun shines once again on unblemished brickwork and pristine surfaces.

But beneath the streets, the drains are slowly clogging up with sand and clay scoured from the walls; the silt also carries billions of flecks of paint, the pulverised words of [——]'s troubled dreams. One day, the gutters will overflow, choking on boasts, threats, and blasphemies; but they'll also cough up the scheme's lost sonnets, epigrams, and parables – its essays, theses, and histories.

Throughout the day, [——]'s ghost-writers sleep, dreaming up new words to answer the toxic roar that, for now, drowns them out, but will not outlast them.

After doing business on his behalf in far flung schemes across the city, McCann's men would slip back into the industrial estate at night to take the chair opposite the Big Man. But by then, they were no longer men. They were foxes, badgers, owls, frogs, rats, relaying information about their activities with furtive glances, tongues flicking at dry lips, bared teeth, blank stares, grimaces.

In each gesture, a story can be read: how much money was taken, how much slipped into back pockets on the way home, the fate of an untrustworthy go-between.

Only Marky Boy can take this seat and retain human form. Each time he returns, he speaks impartially and with precision. This makes him the most dangerous and incomprehensible of all McCann's men. His words are lean and hungry: they have teeth that tear at the truth, ripping through nerve and tendon as they search out meaning.

So McCann sends the boy out, over and over, and each time he comes back, his accounts of what he has seen engulf McCann. The great McCann, blinded by confinement, must in the end come to trust. Marky Boy's eyes are his eyes, and Marky Boy's words are his world.

Over Mark's head, billowing cloud plugs the hole in the roof. McCann feels the warmth of the dog asleep at his feet. He trained him as a pup, but Mark—

'Why should a believe you're tellin the truth?' McCann asks his nephew.

'Because,' replies Mark. 'The truth is what I came here for. And if I ever tell you one word of a lie, if I even think it, I'll be lost forever within your empire.'

2

'Whit is it ye studied again?'

'A clutch of -ologies, I'm afraid, er, social sciences, social policy and the like. With some add-ons.'

As he speaks, Mark steals a glance around the unit and recalls a lecture about light industry bootstrapping regeneration. He imagines the roof intact, fresh white walls, blue overalls—

'Whit kinna add-ons? Let me guess, performin arts?'

'Er, sadly not. My PhD is on the third sector.'

'Shame. You're the best actor av ever seen. Ye play yirsel flawlessly.'

Mark is unsure how to take this; he often finds his uncle difficult to read. McCann's unwavering gaze nudges Mark into prickly self-consciousness. He remembers his first day at the new school, standing at the gate, staring at his brogues.

'A used tae pump a wee actress. Could never tell if she wiz fakin it.'

'Faking? Oh, I see, yeah, right, actresses, eh! I did a bit of theatre in first year actually, nothing serious, but we went to the Fringe that summer. Was good to get back to my old haunts.'

'A know. Av seen aw yer report kerds.'

McCann closes his eyes and rubs his temples. He sees his da, still young, combing Brylcreem through his hair, trimming his tache, pulling on his great coat, flicking invisible oose off his collar: donning his persona for the day's work ahead.

'Ye didny know yer granda.'

'No. What did he do?'

'He wiz the Rent Man, went roon the doors collectin. Or intae pubs, or doon dark alleys if he hid tae. When they built the schemes, he retired.'

'Really?'

'Aye. Then he took up money lendin.'

'Oh. Mum never told me much about when you guys were young.'

'Ye mean, when she wiz young. A wiz born auld, am aulder than that lazy basturt lyin oer by the fields.'

Mark smiles at McCann's reference to the hills that dominate the scheme's view, known locally as The Sleeping Giant.

'So Fettes an Oxford, eh. Chappin doors is in yer blood. That's whit youse dae innit? Gether facts? See whit's whit?'

'In a manner of spea—'

'Just get oot there an suss whit's happenin. Somehin's chainged. A canny shift a gram in ma ain fuckin schemes. Tell me eveyrhin ye see, hear, smell, think.'

Schemes of Bureaucracy (2)

[——] is a scheme of lanes.

Even a short walk bewilders the visitor. Take a few steps down one of its countless narrow lanes and you're soon disoriented, swallowed up in a network of passages that carry you over cascading staircases and leave you drifting through high-hedged canyons. Long, featureless stretches repeat, seemingly ad infinitum, until you're dizzy and lost.

The lanes were mapped out even before the houses, schools, and churches, to counteract the scheme's sprawling layout, and the shortcuts did indeed prove popular. They were handy, traffic free, and filled with neighbours and old acquaintances. You never knew which long lost pal might wander your way next. The lanes bustled with stop-and-chats, gossip, laughter, and tales of days gone by in the vanished slums.

Of course, these endless blethers undermined the planners' key aim: efficiency. Getting things done was difficult with folk ambling from gab to gab. [——]'s pedestrian thoroughfares were inspected by the council's time and motion men, who noted that the average journey by lane now took longer than it would have had the lanes never been built. A major rethink was required, and a bold decision taken: more lanes were needed – many more.

Squads of diggers and tarring teams, dispatched to plough new furrows, scraped past gable ends; burrowed across back courts; drove through middens, sheds, doo huts, and washing greens.

But just as the city's roads department had already found, more lanes simply attract more lane users. This meant more chance meetings, more gossip, and ever more delays to the business of the day.

Now set on their course, the planners would not deviate from their lanes of thinking. They sent their teams back in to sniff out the narrowest spaces between semis, and slot in connecting slipways by uprooting beloved hydrangeas and wiping kids' dens off the map: the lane network exploded. The main lanes were joined left and right by feeder lanes, these in turn fed by tributaries so narrow that small dogs struggled to pass each other peaceably.

People still trudge the lanes, but now they keep their heads down as they pass, so they can dodge the dog faeces. No-one ever looks up, because there's no open sky, only glimpses of cloud between clawing hedges. And above all, no-one dares look left or right, because in every direction there's nothing to see – no houses, gardens, schools or churches, and no way out – just more lanes.

But surely, as any smart schoolkid knows, if you keep one hand on a maze wall, you'll eventually find the exit: that doesn't work here. Take a piece of wood and rattle the railings as you walk; you will inevitably find yourself back where you started. But how can this be? The answer is heard in the distance. Drills, diggers, steamrollers: the lane-builders are still burrowing away, tearing up and renewing the network even as you walk through it.

The lanes are alive, like a knot of worms. Those inside them wander aimlessly, trying to lose themselves, because they have nowhere else to go.

[——] is a scheme of contours.

From the top of the muti-storey tower blocks at the back of the scheme, its undulating terrain rises and falls like a blanket on an unmade bed.

The high ground was once occupied by planners armed with their vision of a new world. They commanded a God's-eye view: decommissioned RAF bombers roared overhead scrawling their message across the sky – A Fresh Start for All! Cameras in bomb bays winked at farms and scattered settlements as every bump in the landscape was captured and indexed.

Back at bomber command, the city's Drawing Office, a meticulously stitched patchwork quilt of photographs was laid out on long desks. Fields were scrutinised and hedgerows traced by yellow-stained fingertips; a sullen farm hand caught glowering at the sky was captured under a magnifying glass; wrecked mine shafts were annotated; avenues of trees crossed out in red ink, as though hit by exploding bombs; old ditches were surrounded by arrows; question marks hung like barrage balloons over old cottages.

The generals of the new age had the future firmly in their sights as they obliterated the past. But as they mulled over their intelligence, anomalies emerged: old roads jerked this way or that, where the direct course seemed logical; fields draped long arms around each other, making complex mosaics of the land; around a small loch, traces of ghostly shorelines extended beyond its reedy edge.

The more the planners pushed their noses into the picture, the more the contours of history reached out to haul them in, enmeshing unkempt eyebrows in thorny hedges; beckoning blinking eyes down dark mineshafts; sucking naïve assumptions into ancient marshes.

Further investigation revealed that the looping roads skirted subsiding mine works, the irregularly shaped fields were terraced to maximise use, and the loch's vast hinterland was a flood plain. So new roads were forced to follow old roads, fixing their eccentricities in tarmac; semis were laid out in tiered crescents around the edges of fields; and the scheme's back streets stopped at the old hedgerows, keeping them clear of the water.

By nesting each change in what came before, the land maps and re-maps itself. From above it's harder to read, but it is possible if you catch it in the right light.

At the top of the flats, you can turn your back on the scheme and look out towards the hills. On a spring morning, you might still see the day the fields were thick with people; they're running, crying, scrambling over crops, ploughing through hedges, trying to reach a pit head obscured by thick black smoke.

[——] is a scheme of deer.

They have the run of the place, roaming the roads and herding in gardens as they please.

Their grazing and nibbling keeps the hedges down, the washing greens trim, and the kerbs free of weeds. But before the deer came, things weren't so neat and tidy. Quad bikers, joyriders, drinkers, tokers, and ravers ruled the streets by day, and gathered in the back courts after dark.

The older residents decided to rid themselves of this anti-social scourge, so the police were called, and the youngsters forced out of the scheme onto the scrubby hinterland beyond the back end.

Here, away from their elders' ears, engines revved, bass-heavy music resonated, and the squeals and laughter of playful seduction tickled the night sky. For a while, everyone was happy with the new arrangement, but the displaced noise began to disturb the wildlife at a nearby nature reserve.

Most agitated were the deer, which for generations had lived there largely unnoticed. Their rowdy new neighbours forced them to break cover and seek refuge elsewhere.

The scheme, now itself a reservation for the quiet and wary, was the deer's best option. They took to its many sheltered niches: the mossy foundations of an unfinished shopping centre, the cloistered remains of a burnt down nursery, overgrown playing fields, bulldozed back streets – the deer made all these habitats their own.

But as their number increased, washing was chewed, flower beds were trampled, gnomes got kicked in the head.

Once again the scheme's seniors acted to rid themselves of a menace. First, they tried gently shooing the deer away, but they were too tame. So more forceful attempts were made, using washing poles and garden forks, but the deer were too nimble. Then a few pensioners sneaked out of the scheme to borrow some quad bikes and speakers while their owners slept off the latest round of partying under the bushes.

The police were soon back in the scheme, this time to investigate theft and enforce a wildlife protection order. The ringleaders were led away, and conditions placed on the other residents guaranteeing peace and tranquillity to all the scheme's creatures.

Now without a care, [——]'s deer strut the streets and herd at the shops, around school gates, in front of the church. The scheme's people are harder to spot, slipping down lanes and cutting through gardens, their range confined to that narrow strip between youth and disdain.

Schemes of Transport (1)

[——] is a scheme of the high seas.

At its launch, a local dignitary smashed a bottle off a gable end and, to great applause, declared [——] the flagship of the city's housing fleet.

Surrounded on all sides by a flat, featureless marsh, its homes were designed along nautical lines, its tenement blocks endowed with staggered tiers of verandas and safety rails painted in battleship grey.

Each flat had a veranda of its own, a quarterdeck from which to gauge the morning sky and chart a smooth course through the day. Bathrooms, kitchens, and close landings were fitted out with small port holes, enabling those inside to batten down the hatches ahead of life's gusty squalls.

Viewed from the street on a clear day, each block carried itself with the aura of a great ocean liner berthed in a tropical lagoon. However, from out on the marsh, seen under grey cloud through bone-chilling drizzle, the scheme could be taken for a grim naval task force heading for some distant conflict.

Nonetheless, on the warm, sunny day of its launch, [——] was a merry flotilla set at full clip, sails billowing, its crews surging onward to dazzling discoveries and unimagined riches.

Yet as the scheme drifted through the years, those fabled treasures remained out of reach – the promised lands always just beyond the horizon.

Nets flung out over rusty handrails caught only the mangy feathers of swooping gulls. Cabin fever raged, and the mood on board grew resentful and mutinous. Water seeped in, trickling down into the sleeping quarters, where dreams of paradise turned soggy and cold. As the vessels creaked and listed, hulls were breached and crews confined below deck, endlessly bailing out.

The relentless elements have wreaked havoc: exteriors, leached of their integrity, are streaked white; flaking handrails give way in the nipping wind; black-green algae smothers portholes, while all around, lapping marsh waters rise.

The gulls' beaks tear at anything thrown overboard, their shrieks drowning out the muffled sounds that escape the deepest holds: clanging chains, babbling tongues.

As you paddle away across the marshes, a pitiless sun hangs overhead. You look back at the scheme of the high seas. In the undulating froth of the treacherous shallows, the city's flagship is adrift: half-sunk, half-mad.

[——] is a scheme of back roads.

As you take the last twist on the road in, the buildings rear up like a gang of highwaymen spread along a turnpike ridge. You pass between them warily, under the watch of verandas, alleys, recesses.

The tenements block off your view of the city beyond, though between them you steal glimpses of spires dwarfed by flats, clusters of office blocks, a tangle of motorways.

But the road on the ridge is a watershed, far upstream from teeming city life –the scheme's streets and lanes run off to the other side, falling away from the glowering heights into a hidden hinterland that swallows you up. The road hairpins down into the scheme and, with each switchback bend, you feel as though you're being passed through some creature's insides, until you reach the scheme's furthest point: the back end.

The road tails off at a block of boarded-up houses, half-swallowed by gathering rubble, dumped refuse, and clumps of weeds. Beyond the tarmac, the back road stumbles into a delta of dirt tracks fanning out across a scrubby plain.

From here, your way forward is uncertain. One path follows faint indentations in the landscape, but quickly loses its way. Another veers off to join a canal before collapsing into a crumbled, dry bank. A third path takes off like a dutiful dog chasing a line of electricity pylons, but soon tires and curls up in the grass at the feet of the loping giants.

To go beyond the back roads is impossible: thornbushes, nettles, potholes, ditches stand in your way; and if you fight your way through, you'll be slowed to a stop by the cloying realisation that, beyond this place, there is nowhere to reach.

You turn to go back, but scratching branches have closed in behind you – you can no longer see the scheme.

Between the high road and the low road, there is a hidden third way: the back roads of [——].

McCann respects the power of words. A deal without a written contract is made verbally, the parties bound by the words they speak. Handshakes engage witnesses who, from that moment, become living verification of the agreement.

Being of such a world, McCann speaks only when necessary. Each word is carefully chosen because words cling to the speaker, forming chains that can never be cast off. Each commitment constrains future actions, and his have brought him to the point of silence, his last order given. A man of his word who can no longer speak can no longer exist.

McCann knows his empire is made of nothing but his words, and now he feels a lifetime of pledges, vows, threats, and demands pressing in on the walls, drumming on the corroded roof, scratching at the stainless-steel door, pounding his temples. He sits at his desk, breathing through his nose, waiting for the pressure of words to ease.

From Mark's side of the desk, words emerge as if from another world, where the spoken word is lighter than air, and words are pinned to paper like butterflies to hold them in place.

But here, words are thicker than blood: not to be spilled carelessly. As Mark's stories flutter into the dense air, they acquire unaccustomed weight and crash to the concrete.

3

'When I was in second year, I tried out for University Challenge. We'd only put ourselves forward for a laugh really, but as it turned out I actually made the team. Then I was kicked off for, er, a disciplinary breach.'

'A disciplinary? At Oxford? Whit did ye dae?'

'Um, there was this girl, and, er, the thing is—'

In a heartbeat, Mark falls back into summer: a minor royal wedding on the lawn, Shakespeare in the park, her brown eyes. He wonders what an Italian diplomat's daughter would make of the unit, with its crumbling concrete columns and corroded beams, the chiaroscuro floor like a chessboard under faltering lights—

'Let me guess, ye got caught in her room.'

'Afraid so. After hours at St Hugh's. They're very strict about that sort of thing there. Very, um, protective. But as it turned out the whole thing was a set up. They had pictures of me climbing in the window and everything.'

'Fuckin phones. Ye didnae bring yours did ye?'

'No I left all my smart devices behind as you said.'

'Good man. So these Shuggy birds, wit wiz their angle?'

'Well you see St Hugh's had their own team in for the series, and they wanted to weaken ours. And as I was told later, it seems they'd identified me as the strongest link.'

'Or the weakest.'

'Ah. Fair point, although I think any of the other lads might have been got at in much the same way.'

'Correct. An there's yer lesson fae yer wee escapade.'

Schemes of Misconstruction (1)

[——] is a scheme of cavities.

Its lofty tower blocks were once Europe's highest, a source of pride to the scheme's residents and those living at its feet. Even prouder was the builder's chief exec, who signed the site off within a near-impossible deadline. This meant the scheme's official opening could take place just before an election, earning him a substantial bonus.

As the labourers reached for the heavens, the project was hailed as a showcase of modern building techniques. But the deadlines were so tight, key elements in its prefab process were overlooked: sections delivered didn't always match up with the plan; here or there a floor and wall might miss by an inch or two.

Foremen, one eye on the calendar, the other on the clock, were forced to find ever more creative solutions. Standard flooring was reclassified as 'semi-mezzanine', external walls relabelled 'verandas'. In some cases, misaligned corners were sealed with newspapers, rags, cigarette packets, or chewing gum – the scheme's backbone was assembled from the bins.

With so many loose ends built into the scheme, it grew into a monument to haste and, soon after election day, the mishaps began, eventually leading to a disastrous partial collapse.

Such was the frequency of these events, and the inadequate official response, that the residents took matters into their own hands: a team of small boys was assembled, the sort most at home on top of wardrobes, or dreepying from ledges, or squeezing through a cat flap when someone forgot their key.

The lads were given licence to explore [——]'s nooks and crannies, on condition that they fix the construction abuses as they went along. The recruits felt as though they'd been given the world's biggest Meccano set, and were soon working round the clock to make good the shortcomings, which were so obvious that even a small child without any building trade experience had no trouble spotting them.

As they went along, they widened shafts, ducts, and vents so their older pals and siblings could join them. Once the girls broke through the scheme's

polystyrene ceiling, its dead space was quickly transformed into a catacomb of comfy dens.

The adults were content to leave them to it because, in the absence of youth clubs and community centres, the kids were at least out of harm's way. They had also put a stop to catastrophic structural failures, so on both scores the grown-ups slept easier in their beds.

In time, [——]'s youth came to feel most at home inside the cavities, sheltered from an indifferent world and the cloying demands of the parents forever banging on their walls. But as the children grew within their confined world, it began to feel cramped, so the hollow spaces had to grow with them.

Meanwhile, on the other side, the bedrooms, kitchens, and hallways were inching smaller. One day, the grown-ups, by now longing to see their kids – and grandkids, whom they knew only by their footfall – decided to join the youngsters' ever-expanding domain.

If you look up at the towers from outside, you'll see only boarded windows; on the landings, front doors are barred. These flats might look abandoned, but they harbour a teeming, inside-out community which lives life to the full: in [——], the most solid thing is emptiness.

Schemes of Aesthetics (2)

[——] is a scheme of gardens.

It was envisioned as a leafy garland on the city's brow, so prospective tenants were scrutinised by the housing office, and only those with the greenest fingers handed keys.

Its streets, nested like rose petals, presented lawns dissected by delightfully meandering paths; flower beds were sprinkled all around, each a blank canvas for the scheme's new live-in floriculturists.

The enthusiastic newcomers wasted no time summoning up a stunning first summer's bloom. Their carnival of colour exceeded all expectation and, at the first time of asking, the scheme won a prestigious national garden competition.

Encouraged by this early success, the local gardeners began fully to express themselves, conjuring from the soil an abundance of wonders: window boxes erupted on every ledge; from Babylonian baskets, tendrils trickled down walls; new varieties of flower, unique to the scheme and thus suffixed '[——]ensis', appeared everywhere – even the phone boxes were made mini-tropics.

Through long summer evenings, the gardeners would work till dark, then drop exhausted under towering stalks of rhubarb; or stretch out aching backs on undulating canna lilies; or soothe sunburnt limbs with Persian ivy: [——] truly was a garden of the gods.

Having trounced all comers in all categories, the residents' only remaining competitive outlet was the struggle to outdo each other, so intra-scheme street championships were arranged. These were fiercely fought, but with so little to choose between one stunning display and the next, the judges' decisions were a lottery. This led to appeals, counter-appeals, and protests; but unable to explain their choices to the losers' satisfaction, the judges found themselves challenged in the streets, and even subjected to verbal abuse.

With a new tone set, disputes quickly spilled into open argument over trellis fences. Festering side issues – the shade thrown by a tree, the origin of an aphid attack, the root cause of low hose pressure – proliferated like weeds.

Some say the scheme died the day the sabotage began. Things certainly went downhill rapidly thereafter: what had taken years to nurture was laid waste in the blink of a petunia.

But worse, the overuse of herbicides on garden paths and borders was slowly poisoning the scheme's water table, with deadly effect. No-one had noticed that amid the growing rancour, petals were losing their lustre and verdant lawns developing alopecia.

By the time the last lawn turned black, the stench of rotting vegetation hung heavy over the scheme, and acrid, stagnant pools covered washing greens: the residents were forced to leave. When [——]'s last desiccated leaf blew away, there was no-one left to mourn the bare brown earth and dusty streets.

All that was lovingly planted and nurtured is uprooted, discarded. But one reminder of the old days still remains. The gardeners had installed gargantuan gnomes proportionate to their award-winning produce. Now they lie toppled in the gutters, or piled up like scrums of drunken Brobdingnagians. One sits alone on the kerb, smiling like an idiot, fishing in the wind, as if trying to catch a lost dream.

Schemes of Transport (2)

[——] is a scheme of treasure.

It nestles in the loop of a canal that swings off the straight course to avoid old mines. The houses come right down to the canal bank, ending where a cottage row once stood. A few weathered sandstone blocks still lie scattered around, now seats in the sun for anglers, daytime drinkers, and weary walkers.

The original mining community fell to ruin after a heavily laden boat misjudged the turn and capsized. As the stricken crew was helped onto the towpath, the vessel was relieved of its load. Cured hams, blocks of lard, barrels of sugar, dried herring, and cases of whiskey were smuggled into the reeds.

Deep into the night, the cottagers ate and drank as never before. But as they slept off their good fortune, the dawn peace was shattered by the rap of bailiffs' sticks. Searches were made of the cottages, and the suspects, many barely dressed, dragged from their beds and marched through the fields – to conviction, sacking, and eviction.

During the desolate winter that followed, a young mother called Mary, formerly of the row, was found floating face down in the icy water, emaciated and blue.

In the decades to come, there would be more shipping mishaps on the cursed banks of the loop, and more stricken canal boats mysteriously relieved of their cargos. Nearby dwellings were routinely searched, but no contraband was ever recovered.

These misfortunes were attributed to tight turns catching navigators unaware, or counter currents sucking the vessels off course – but there were also other theories.

On the loop's towpaths at dusk, horses would suddenly

frighten; bargemen spoke of seeing strange lights on the water; there were whispers of a woman emerging from the depths. Some saw a hollow face, others a grasping hand in the reeds. Years later, one man swore he'd seen Mary's derelict cottage dimly lit by a flickering lamp.

Mary's story became legend the length of the canal. Mothers would whisper her name to keep children from playing too near the water's edge; in time they would tell their children the same tales. Eventually, Mary's abandoned row was demolished, but her story survived.

Today, locals in dire straits sometimes take a seat on the stones by the water and remember Mary. Depending on your predicament, you might spot a banknote lying on the towpath; or, when the foodbank is empty, a few tins of baby food might suddenly turn up in a plastic bag swinging from a tree; or maybe a lost loved one will smile back at you from the canal's smooth surface, calming a storm of the heart.

Life on the loop is still hard, but no misery is endured in vain. The scheme's people count themselves richer than most, because the land is laden with treasure – the story of their past.

Schemes of The Past (2)

[——] is a scheme of pitches.

At its heart is a hole: a no-go zone for wandering joyriders, land-hungry house builders, short-cutting cyclists, and curious dogs.

You reach it by descending through streets full of the comings and goings of the day. Then, where the tarmac ends, life comes to a stop. Your first impression is of a landlocked, drought-stricken sea: the scheme hangs over it like a jacked-up shoreline, an outcrop on the edge of oblivion.

You look out on an expanse of red blaes football pitches. As you climb down towards them, you begin to feel uneasy. Then the emptiness rushes you like a bore tide – you begin to panic – flatness plays tricks on the eye, confounding your sense of scale: as you move further in, the scheme's receding rooftops form an unbroken horizon which could be the encircling inner wall of a crater on the far side of Mars.

Your feet crunch on the regolith, and you find a measure of perspective: you're crossing the lattice of rectangles and circles that mark out the pitches. On such barren ground, these faint lines could be scars inflicted on a dying world by its last suffering inhabitants.

Overhead, the sun crosses the sky like a goalkeeper's kickout seeking a head. But its edge is blurred, smoothed away as if by abrasion by a billion particles in the air. Its light is filtered, sprinkling pinks and reds across the pitches – your hands have turned to coral.

The day's first thermals stir the dust, and transparent sheets flutter in the air. The microclimate whips up its own breeze that skims the surface and flits around posts and crossbars; silk veils rise up to dance in empty goalmouths.

As the swirling ash thickens, it coalesces into dust devils. You cover your face, and from between your fingers you glimpse caravans of cowled figures leaning into the wind: these ghostly lines might be lost football teams seeking their pitches. One player seems to be carrying a ball on his back – or maybe he's a camel. Out here in the vastness of the unnumbered, unnamed pitches you could wander for a lifetime and never find your match, instead trudging away your years wrapped up in a blinding blizzard.

The wind howls and passing figures give way to fleeting mirages, hints of lobes and limbs. The stinging air brings you to your knees; teeth in the ground tear at your flesh – the pitches are alive, teeming with creatures once trapped in ancient sediment. They swim again in your blood; you feel them coursing through your veins, driving at your heart.

It's getting late. The sun hangs low; dark, discoloured, bloated – a dying red giant crashing down on your head.

Schemes of Perception (1)

[——] is a scheme of reflections.

You step off the bus and find yourself alone at a row of shops. Most are closed, their metal shutters bolted to the ground. Only the one at the far end is open; you walk towards it.

Along the front of the row, concrete bollards stick out of the ground at odd angles. All are cracked, chipped, or broken. Passing between them feels like entering a dragon's mouth.

They guard a squat single-storey building with a shallow-angled roof. It is crowned with a tangle of anti-climb spikes and tufts of barbed wire. The drainpipes are smeared with brown grease. The gable end shows traces of bricked up windows. Where the pebble dash has crumbled, there's a ghost of an old staircase running up the side of the building.

As you pass, you notice the brick columns between the windows have been pockmarked by graffiti-busting sand blasters. The stores' names seem familiar: the bright plastic livery of the betting shop appears in many schemes, but this is the flagship, proudly proclaiming the name of a man who bet everything on the weakness of others. Next is a beauty salon, its emblem an angry eyebrow and fearsome claws ready to pounce. This props up a skinny, no-frills off licence.

The general store sprawls over the last few units. Its windows are laden with toys, cheap jewellery, cleaning products, long life foodstuffs, and more: a jam-packed bazaar overwhelms the eye. You focus on a garish red novelty clock whose numbers run backwards; the display seems to swirl around it.

Something in the panes catches your attention – clouds swimming, a slash of green, a red-and-white streak: a building.

You turn and see a second row of shops.

You approach its forecourt. There are no bollards; instead, the row is fronted by a strip of freshly mown grass. Over the windows, candy-striped awnings flutter in the breeze. They form a loose canopy along the parade. Across its entire length, one name is proclaimed in art-deco Bakelite:

CO-OPERATIVE SOCIETY

Bread, milk, and tinned goods; hardware items; kitchen utensils; and clothing are methodically laid out in its windows. There are flats above, each with a blooming window-box.

At the far end of the parade is a red phone box. Inside, a woman dusts the directory, waters a vase of flowers, then steps out and runs up the stairs at the side of the building. At the top, as she disappears round the back, she drops something: a small piece of paper flutters down to the tiles. You call out, but she doesn't hear.

The Co-Op's windows catch your eye; something's rushing towards you; you spin round and it's right there, nudging your nose, cold and hard: you're pressed up against glass. You step back and find you're back at the general store. You see the novelty clock, its numbers no longer reversed, the second hand moving forward.

No-one else is around. There's no bus, and no second row of shops behind you. You find an old piece of paper at your feet and stoop to pick it up.

It's a Co-Op membership card. No name is written on it, but it's stamped, in bold art-deco letters:

EXPIRED

A blade of sunshine plunges through the hole in the roof, piercing the powdery air. In its swirling wisps, McCann sees the tatters of his plan.

He pulls his nephew's words around him like armour. They confirm what he already knows, that in the end, all plans fail; complexity lays tripwires; intention is booby trapped.

He stands and moves towards the light. He remembers starting out, the whole world within his reach, his rush to fill every niche – like a burn tumbling downhill, taking on the shape of the day.

Peering up at a chink of sky, he tries to pinpoint the moment things changed; the decision or indecision, action or inaction, that led him to this dead end.

Trapped in the unit, time no longer holds meaning for McCann. Swamped by the unseen, he can neither understand the past, nor predict the future. The dancing dust holds no answers. Where once he surfed a swelling tide of chaos, now he drowns under its crashing weight.

As he goes under, he knows he's being watched: by creditors, former allies, the police. But above all, he feels on him the eyes of those other McCanns, the men he might have become had he chosen the paths untaken.

He was always haunted by glimpses of himself in others. He once saw his dimpled chin on a triad's face, his nose under a Turkish courier's cap, his jawline carried off by a Latvian bodyguard through a fir forest clearing.

Now he avoids mirrors because it's unsettling to see so much of himself at once. It feels safer to be spread across the globe, divided into small pieces, hidden in plain sight. Being concentrated in one place feels reckless, indulgent.

Mark, his words turbo charged by bold gestures and facial expressions, seems alien to McCann. Yet, for the first time, he sees something of himself in his nephew; though not in his creasing forehead, bobbing eyebrows, or gesturing hands: Mark has the young McCann's cohesion – his fluidity, his lost flow.

4

'Ye look knackered – been partyin?'

'Not quite,' Mark answers, stifling a yawn. 'I was up all night chasing a deadline for my thesis.'

McCann turns his seat and swings up his boots, clattering the desk. 'Whit's it aboot?'

'It's called 'Public Private Partnerships Since World War Two: Synergies and Dysergies.'

'Happy wi it?'

'We'll see. If it's worth a doctorate, I'll be happy.'

McCann rises to his feet. 'A doctorate eh?' He loops behind Mark towards a pile of boxes.

'I'm hopeful. Well, cautiously optimistic.' Mark cranes his neck left and right, eager not to appear rude. 'Fingers crossed! I've given it my best shot!' he shouts.

'Aw emdy can ask,' McCann whispers in his ear. 'C'mere n gies a haun.'

McCann leads the way. He wrests the top box from the pile; Mark's outstretched arms take a small portion of its weight, and they start shuffling awkwardly towards the desk.

'So synergies, whit's that aboot?'

'In the context of my thesis... or generally?' Mark gasps.

'Baith.'

'It's when two agents combine...to greater effect...than either could achieve...individually.' Mark feels his forearms burning. McCann adjusts himself, relieving Mark of his token effort, though he still feels obliged to keep his arms under the box.

'I found that state agencies and private sector interests synergise best where there's transparency, to counteract the accountability deficit born from market sensitivity and the merry-go-round of changing faces in national and local *governme—'*

'An that other wan ye mentioned?'

'Dysergy.'

'Fill me in, a don't huv Google.'

'Well that's the opposite, when a combined effort is less effective than either party might achieve separately.'

'Three, two, wan,' McCann warns, inviting Mark to withdraw his arms.

THUD!

'A wouldny worry. Sounds lit yer doctorate's in the bag.'

'Well it's, er, in the hands of the gods now.'

'Int we aw?' McCann sighs, conjuring a flick knife from between his fingers. He plunges it between the box's flaps, slitting the tape from end to end; Mark suppresses a shiver.

'Ye know me an yer da were in business the gither?'

'Yes.'

'Did yer maw tell ye anyhin?'

'Er, not really. She's never said much about...things.'

'Well we had wan a they synergies gaun. Big time.'

'Then dad died.'

'Aye.'

'Then I went to my new school.'

'Aye.'

[——] is a scheme of statues.

The first was erected to celebrate a favourite son's glory laden football career; his unveiling was a proud occasion.

Because he'd played on one side of the city's football divide, the other team's fans sought their own hero. They soon found their man. A minor star admittedly, not as gifted as the maestro whose grin now graced the scheme, but a local lad nonetheless, and as far as his advocates were concerned, one of their own.

After the second inauguration, a third local footballer emerged, a youngster inspired by his two predecessors, but better than both. He stormed the big Euro leagues and became the face of a global brand, so it seemed only fair that he be appointed the third icon of the shopping circus.

His ribbons were barely cut when a local snooker player scored a stunning success by winning a big tournament, and so applause rang out again as another cast-iron behemoth was dropped into place by a groaning crane.

'But why only sport?' muttered some. 'And just men?' asked others. 'After all, we've got our very own pop star!' The girl in question was in the middle of a successful three week run on a TV talent show, and her debut single had just entered a local downloads chart: this decided the matter. And so there were five.

The circus shoppers and hangers-about now had a range of plinths to sit on, with a variety of clenched fists, trophies, snooker cues, and mike stands on which to hang their bags as they basked in the sun.

Local traders were delighted; business had never been brisker, with the shops fast becoming a tourist magnet as people from neighbouring schemes flocked to see [——]'s avenue of achievers.

But the restless energy that had propelled so many of the scheme's folk to success prompted more debate. The community council was accused of glorifying celebrity culture. Surely, the argument went, the scheme's young people might be better served looking up to its real heroes, who day in day out delivered meals on wheels, cared for the vulnerable, or nursed the sick?

The sentiment was broadly welcomed, so three more local women joined the Circus immortals, bringing gender parity to the plinths. Cases were made for other noteworthy citizens: beloved teachers, lollipop men, dinner ladies, paperboys and papergirls; and so the statues multiplied, until the local churches opined that every last resident, being of infinite value in the eyes of God, should be celebrated equally – thus began the monumental task of erecting a statue to everyone.

With blocks of granite and iron being dropped off on every patch of spare ground – sculptors chiselling, welders' guns sparking, and soldering irons fizzling through the night – life for the scheme's residents became unbearable.

Sadly, many fled before seeing themselves set in place. All ran without looking back, and by the time the work was complete, everybody was gone.

Now [——]'s people wave in the rain, or stride out to a crucial appointment, or recline in the garden, or pirouette on a wall, forever imbued with the sheer joy of being alive in a world full of possibilities. But in a scheme full of statues, there are none.

[——] is a scheme of perfection.

It started as an architect's vision and became an agenda item at a committee meeting. Then, just as a form was being filled in, a phone rang, causing tea to be spilled over a cluttered desk. Amid the confusion, on the soggy, wrinkled form, YES was ticked instead of NO, and [——] was officially complete before work on it had even begun.

This meant the scheme, still only a pending project, was factored into the city's maintenance budget, which was embedded in the council's financial plan, which exerted a pull on the nationwide local authority spending formula.

As the amount of money involved was initially small, the mistake wasn't noticed for several years. But by the time it was spotted, no-one wanted to admit to it because resources allocated to the scheme were being used to alleviate shortfalls in maintenance budgets elsewhere, and as under-funding worsened, officials were in no position to own up to a multi-year overspend that would be clawed back.

So [——], the perfect scheme where nothing was ever spent on repairs because nothing ever went wrong, was officially written into the accounts, where it looked every bit as real as its physical counterparts.

To consolidate the illusion, the scheme's unwalked streets were named, its ghost houses allocated numbers and postcodes, and its shadow schools placed on official lists. The scheme even featured on a leaflet aimed at tourists, titled The City's Hidden Gems, which boasted of its perfection while underlining the impossibility of ever reaching it by public transport. Finally, it was marked on Ordinance Survey maps in an inhospitable corner of the city's far-flung edge.

As ever more departments – street cleaning, youth work, road markings, mental health outreach – found their budgets squeezed tighter, these services grew ever more reliant on resources siphoned off from [——]. Its unopened textbooks were diverted to hard up schools elsewhere; street lighting repair teams, never troubled by a faulty bulb in [——], were free to throw light on the city's other dark corners; home helps, untroubled by [——]'s self-sufficient old folk, ran errands across town. The city where everything went wrong was propped up by the scheme where nothing ever did.

And as the cuts bit deeper, the non-existent scheme grew bigger, throwing its protective ring around ever more of the city's most vulnerable residents.

[——]'s architect, now nearing retirement, recently had another dream. This time his vision is even grander: an entire city of perfection, requiring no maintenance at all, because nothing would ever break, age, or decay. Of course, implementing this would mean the existing city, with all its flaws, would have to be completely razed.

The perfect city is currently marked as a pending project, and somebody just put the kettle on.

[——] is a scheme of buses.

Each morning a blanket of mist obscures the sun. From the top of the hill, everything below is hidden, except a jumble of mud-brown rooftops.

Around midday, as the last trailing hems of wispy fog are gathered up out of the road's deepest dip, you realise you've not been looking at a scheme at all, but a collection of buses.

Through the afternoon, the vehicles sit steaming in silence. Parked haphazardly, they nudge each other at curious angles. Single and double-deckers abut microbuses; an airport sprinter, trapped in the crush, peeks out as if struggling for breath; the rusty cranes of abandoned recovery vehicles hang over them, dripping condensation onto roofs.

Seen from above, the melee looks like a paused stock car race. The positions are only changed by nudges from new arrivals. With the winter's first freeze, fingers of fog will lead the next bus astray, pointing the way down as it skids to its new resting place at the back of the line.

This unforgiving trap, known locally as The Glen, might have been scratched in the earth by a huge talon. The road through it, the only way into the scheme beyond, plummets and climbs at gradients best suited to an acrobatic biplane.

Within The Glen's warped landscape, radios and phones don't work. So as they settle at the lowest point, drivers are forced to abandon their vehicles and haul themselves up the ice to safety, clinging to the railings that run up the side of the road. By then, the victims know there's no point in sending for help, because that would only damn another hapless driver to the same fate.

The oldest buses have been here for as long as anyone can remember. As the years pass, their once proud liveries fade and flake. Some buses have collapsed in on themselves: tyres perish in the glaur; undercarriages rust into the earth.

Such is the reputation of this savage natural barrier, they say that were the city ever to fall to invaders, the fleeing council would risk all on this road in the hope of finding sanctuary in the fabled scheme beyond The Glen.

Schemes of Perception (2)

[——] is a scheme of misdirection.

Knuckles of cloud hang over the rooftops, and the tenements on the ridge appear to flinch. Half hidden in the drizzle, they could be forgotten standing stones once aligned with some flighty star, or a cortege of coffins lost in the smir en route to the graveyard. As you get closer, a half-glimpsed gable end might be a riot cop's shield; or a Roman soldier's, buffeted by exploding squalls hurled by unruly hills.

It's only when you enter the closes that signs of everyday life emerge. You see a carved wooden nameplate beside a wicker basket dangling lavender over a spotless glossy threshold. On the landing above, you notice kids' muddy football boots and a plastic trike. Then you spot yourself in the door opposite, your reflection warped by rivets hammered into its stainless-steel panels, your mangled features flicking round their ragged edges.

But you must disregard these clues about the lives lived here, because in [——], nothing is at it seems. Behind those hanging baskets is a dank, bare-floored giro drop; step over the jumble of toys into the flat above and you'll experience the tropical microclimate of a leafy, aromatic jungle, a forbidden zone nourished by UV light; and the face-dissembling door shields a tranquil place, a softly lit sanctuary where visitors take comfort · in fine clothes, rich perfumes, and exclusive accessories brought here from the city by skinny boys in fat jackets.

In [——], nothing can be taken at face value. Not doors, nameplates, labels, clothes, eyes, or even words: this is where truth comes to hide, on a shape-shifting ridge under enveloping cloud.

Schemes of Memory (2)

[——] is a scheme of starlings.

When the bulldozers came, the sky turned black with birds. As their treetop homes tumbled, they scribbled their confusion in the sky with tangled whirls and loops, until [——]'s roofs and ledges offered new places of refuge.

Each autumn evening, the scheme's people would gather at their windows and verandas to watch the starlings dive and soar, swirl and turn, merge and diverge.

To their delight, they soon realised the birds weren't just forming random shapes, but rather, in their choreographed movements, they were painting pictures – and even better, these pictures told a story.

All the sequences began with panic: the day the humans turned the earth inside out. Then the starlings flew back to an earlier time, when a thick canopy covered the land. Next, the trees vanished, and the ground was criss-crossed by tiny divisions, making it look like a plaid blanket, over which men and women crawled, bent double, indistinguishable from the animals.

People loved the displays. Especially popular were the endings depicting the present day. Aligning nose to tail, the starlings formed gossamer filaments and weaved themselves into a 3D map of the whole scheme, finally zooming in on specific blocks and gardens. Each night the featured spots would change, keeping the shows fresh and exciting.

But issues of interpretation arose. Where the ice-cream van driver might see a crowd of children flocking round her van, a busy housewife might recall the day her washing line snapped, and a cranky old man might spot a rowdy gang running wild through the backs. Did a tight, falling formation allude to a summer's night's game of kerby? Or the half brick that smashed a school window? Or a car hitting the surgery?

Different readings of the birds' movements eventually caused heated argument. People began to shout and jostle during the displays, acrimony rising into the air, forming ugly vortices beneath the hypersensitive starlings. The birds began to panic, their clean lines and slick shapes breaking down into the irregular forms that heralded the scheme's construction.

But these signs of distress were barely noticed amid the tumult on the streets. Then, one evening, when no-one was looking up anymore, the birds flew away.

Down in [——], beneath empty skies, people are still struggling to make themselves heard over all the screaming. One day, somebody will look up and remember the fleeting shapes that once filled the void, and finally understand what the starlings were really trying to say: that by moving in harmony, people have reshaped the land many times, and can do so again.

The sun splits the desk in half.

Sitting back in shadow, McCann absorbs Mark's stories. From the golden side of the desk, the boy throws light on the empire's darkest corners. For McCann, listening to others is a proprietary act, so Mark's insights, suppositions, and guesses – his voice even – become his own.

Squinting into the sunlight, Mark feels his words being swallowed by the void. He reaches deeper for meaning, but the more clearly he describes the schemes, the more he loses himself. As he talks, his lips start to tingle; his tongue feels heavy, as if numbed by a dentist's needle; his own voice sounds distant; his accent and diction, the structure of his sentences, odd. He's breathing differently too: shallow, fast, blood thundering in his ears.

When Mark has no more words to give, McCann reaches under his chair and hauls up a dusty scroll. He spreads it across the desk and gestures to Mark to pin down the corners. Between their hands, Mark sees familiar streets and empty fields, but the map is confusing. As he tries to follow his old route to school, the way is blocked off by a forest of unfamiliar markings and symbols: arrows, squares, triangles.

The sun creeps over the roof, and self-knowledge leeches across the desk. McCann sees himself in the map, standing at the centre of a great X; a crossroads of past and future. But all its branches are dead, snapping under their own weight. He knows that tomorrow he'll be carved up and will vanish into the great kaleidoscope. Everybody who ever lived will be there too, split, cut, parcelled, recut, dispersed, and scattered to all the corners of the globe. McCann sees the human race as the perfect stash, where the dead hide inside the living, their unsuspecting mules, who walk the streets, fix their hair, lie in bed, fuck themselves silly, slicing and dicing themselves over and over, flushing themselves away as the battering ram smashes through the front door – always just a bit too late.

5

Screams bounce back off the walls; Mark squirms in his seat. The man lying on his front scrambles to hold on, until his knuckles are smashed. Then he's flipped onto his back and dragged; hammers fall on his skinny limbs and light frame until he's still.

'Seen enough?' McCann chuckles, pressing the pause button. 'That scheme wiz just a big waiting room. We wur bored oot wur nuts. We used tae go aboot wreckin the place, then this hing turns up.' He drums his fingers on the battered black box under the TV screen. A hollow clang resonates within.

'The VCR,' Mark states, as if to reassure himself that the grainy image still flickering on the screen is from a film.

'That's wur first pirate. A taped it aff the telly. Naebody else recorded it, so we passed it aboot, gave hauf the school a shot, then went roon collectin hire fees. A couple a teachers seen it tae, gave them a freebie tae pull them in. Yer da thought this wiz gonny chainge the world.'

'And did it?'

'In a wiy.' McCann walks to the wall and slides out a brick. 'He wiz the bookkeeper, there's his first book.'

He throws a black notebook at Mark, who fumbles it onto his lap. Some sections hang loose from the binding. Aligning its dog-eared pages, he flicks through them, recognising his dad's handwriting.

'Are these your customers?' It reads like a directory of the scheme. Mark skims the names. Many are familiar; most have numbers written beside them in pencil.

'By the time a left school it wiz aw in here,' McCann says, tapping his temple. 'A memorized, every name, every debt, plus who was stayin where they wurny supposed tae, who liked whit kinna films, who wiz intae the dodgy stuff. We startit *daein them an all. Came in fae Amsterdam.'*

'Hence these coded numbers in the margins.'

'Then later oan we diversified wur imports.'

The TV picture shimmers and folds in on itself. Black and silver streaks writhe across the screen: like the last thing a fish sees while being reeled in, Mark thinks, pushing the old book of secrets across the desk.

'By then we hid contacts, customers, an a scheme full a numb nuts climbin the woz. The next step wiz easy.' McCann taps the book, keeping his gaze on Mark. 'Cos naebdy says 'naw' tae the bookkeeper.' From the VCR comes a clicking sound; McCann takes the book back to the wall. 'We hid plenty a message boays willin tae dae us a turn.'

'So the business had, er, lots of goodwill,' Mark suggests.

The noise from the machine gets louder, the screen resolving to a grey fuzz. Inside, cogs screech. The tape snaps and spools loose, as if trying to scratch its way out.

McCann pokes his fingers through the flap and wrenches out the cassette. He presents it to Mark as if it were a newborn baby, its broken tape trailing across the desk like an umbilical cord. Mark takes it and reads the film title, written on a dirty label in his dad's hand:

A SENSE OF FREEDOM

[——] is scheme of nods.

As the old slums came down, the planners compared them with the prosperous suburbs and found something remarkable: the slums contained an abundance not only of rats, germs, and filth, but words.

Women out shopping would regularly stop and chat, often with listening children in tow; drunk men clinging to walls regaled incredulous youngsters with tall tales; angry squabbles spilled out of overcrowded flats into echoing stairwells, harsh words ricocheting up and down stairs like gunfire around playing children. The slums, while materially poor, were rich at least in respect of the spoken word.

Whereas, the social surveyors found, out in the suburbs the converse was true: the actuary with his key in the front door would pretend not to have seen the estate agent on the front step over the hedge; Freemason and Rotarian brushed past in the street with no more than a raised eyebrow; and verbal exchanges between ladies in tearooms were like eighteenth century duels – formal, brief, and conclusive.

Armed with this data, two inescapable conclusions were reached: one, the number of words spoken per person per square foot is inversely proportional to personal wealth; and two, any remedy for the living conditions of the poor must therefore stem the flow of words.

So the finest minds in planning created a new type of environment. Public spaces would be made as forbidding as possible: gusty, grey bowls were constructed, forcing women to quicken their pace, avert their gaze, clutch at their coats, and clamp their lips; pubs, traditionally great tongue looseners, were kept miles from the new homes; and signs were erected demanding Strictly No Ball Games on ground where children might be tempted to play team sports involving communication.

And, to ensure stray words didn't coalesce into lengthy chats, people were sealed off in a new kind of street that ran perpendicular to the ground. In this disorienting cliff-edge world, minding your own business and keeping yourself to yourself became new virtues of the poor, as they'd always been in suburbia.

The system is now self-policing. You can walk [——]'s streets for days without hearing a single word spoken out loud. Idle blether and playful banter are unknown. People speak only in dire emergency, and even then, tersely, concisely.

Instead of talking, people converse by nodding. An outsider might think this would allow only for passing greetings and general agreement, but the residents have devised a secret language of subtle neck movements more elaborate and elegantly expressive than spoken English.

The social engineers still watch, listen, and measure, but the residents don't utter a word to them, because they know that if they say too much – if they say anything at all – the wrecking ball will swing again.

Schemes of Coercion (3)

[——] is a scheme of candles.

Tiny flames sprout in clusters, swaying and jerking near broken walls, wrecked traffic islands, and smashed bus shelters.

The strengthening breeze makes the flames flicker, their light coming and going as if shared with another world. On windy days, they singe the pavements, leaving scorch marks around shards of plastic, wrenched wing mirrors, and rubber streaks on the tarmac.

Passers-by linger, then go about their morning as if driven by the whipping wind. They step between the candles' blackened wicks with narrowed eyes, clamped jaws, and pursed lips. The prevailing westerly gives people the look of mannequins, as if made to buckle and crumple, their lives slow-motion tests of the limits of durability.

In the main square, all is calm, the day like any other. Shop windows catch the dull light of a pallid sky; blackbirds peck at the mud; children chase one another.

As the sky darkens, you hear the wind pick up again. It wraps itself round the scheme, racing, revving, quickening its heart.

But this wind sounds different; its soul is mechanical. You realise the night is ruled by a different force of nature, one that seeks out youth. It thrums in the air and rumbles in the ground, calling them away from the scheme, carrying them out into the suburbs. Then the force slams into reverse, sucking them back in, and they head home at breakneck speed, chasing their tails, burning up the night.

They return transformed, re-entering the scheme as conquerors on gilded chariots parading the spoils of victory.

Windows down, screaming, they are masters of the wind, cutting through frictionless space, their flesh and bone converted to streaks of blinding light on full beam. As they feed the screeching engine of night, decades are burned up in seconds: they pulverize time, glowing like candles which, for an instant, outshine all the stars in the sky.

[——] is a scheme of empties.

Each terraced house, semi, and tenement flat, is, and always has been, empty.

On their first day on site, the foremen, labourers, and tradesmen were told that under no circumstances should they set foot inside the buildings they were constructing, and warned that failure to comply would result in instant dismissal.

So overhead pulleys, underground trolleys, telescopic poles, and long-handled brushes were rigged up, and innovative techniques devised to get the job done. The challenge tested the foremen's ingenuity and the squads' gymnastic ability but, in the end, the work was completed within spec and without mishap.

To finish the job, each pristine new home had three-inch thick shutters, fashioned from a new, secret steel alloy, bolted tight to its windows and doors. A similar cap was fitted on the chimney, to keep the interiors sealed off from weather and time.

Today, overgrown dandelions nuzzle at the shutters, as though trying to sample the forbidden darkness within. At night, small mammals sniff out the scheme's abandoned subterranean tunnels and paw at its unyielding foundations. But each night the flowers droop their heads in disappointment and, by the next day, the creatures have abandoned their efforts to go foraging elsewhere.

However, since being installed, the shutters have faced another test of their integrity, under which they groan and creak, warp and stretch. A rumour blows around these empty streets that the shutters are sensitive to an ethereal force which shapes everything around us, but of which we're largely unaware: that each life lived is moulded by the countless unlived lives which, by their close proximity, exert an invisible pressure on our hopes and desires, shaping our dreams and cities.

In [——], the ratio of lives unlived to those lived is infinitely high, so with each passing day, the invisible force grows stronger and, by degrees, the shutters yield, becoming ever more concave.

When this mounting pressure finally forces an opening – works loose a brick, dislodges a tile, or even pokes a knot out of a floorboard – then nothing in the universe will be able to prevent the scheme, maybe even the whole world, from being sucked inside.

But for now [——]'s metal cataracts gaze on, blindly inverting suns and moons, moons and suns.

[——] is a scheme of grey.

After its construction, the painters were sent in to realise a bold vision. They daubed the scheme's doors, window frames, guttering, pipes, closes, and external walls, grey: the aim was to demonstrate the harmony that can be found in the subtle blend of identical elements.

The tenants were warned against altering the paintwork – even the tiniest splash of colour was strictly forbidden. But the scheme's artistic merit was soon questioned, its drab outlook blamed for migraines, nausea, and depression. Some sufferers complained to the local housing office, only to be told their achromatic surroundings reflected the architect's view that all life is a continuum of light and darkness, so their ailments were integral to the piece. An admin assistant, however, also let slip that during the scheme's construction, the council had acquired a large batch of unwanted grey paint from the MOD.

So [——]'s future looked grey, until one day a cracked windowsill needed some Polyfilla. The resultant blueish white streaks panicked the occupier into touching it up with some grey paint she found in the shed and, to her relief, it matched perfectly. But she was later horrified to find it had dried in a touch lighter. Panicking, she painted the whole windowsill. Then, realising she now had an odd window out, did the rest of them too, along with the walls.

The next morning, a crowd gathered at her hedge. She was asked if she'd ever been tested for colour blindness. She hadn't. To laughter and applause, she was informed that she'd painted her whole house canary yellow.

By the end of the day, the scheme was a riot on the retina, with rainbow four-in-a-blocks, pink polka dot semis, technicolour tenements, and psychedelic high flats.

The council's initial response was ignored. In this new scheme, breach of tenancy letters just weren't that eye-catching anymore. Meanwhile, the flourishes grew richer and more daring. There were stripes, wavy lines, crazy chevrons; some threw paint-filled balloons at their walls, until the scheme looked like the front line in a paintball war.

The maintenance department sent in its best painters to wipe out the Multicoloured Revolution, but its plodding workforce proved no match for the scheme's inspired divisions of Pollocks and Rothkos: time and again, the greys found themselves outflanked and outbrushed.

Then the council deployed its heavy artillery. Invoices were dropped through letterboxes, itemising charges for painters' call outs, labour time, and materials. In the end, it was that greyest of sciences – economics – that won it.

Or did it? By now, the locals had developed a sophisticated appreciation of colour, and with it, a regard for the subtler shades of action required to win a tactical battle. The tenants' association requested that uplighters be installed in each garden so people might enjoy the scheme's unique charms around the clock. Delighted by this new support for the status quo, the council agreed.

At the big switch on, officials applauded as bright lamps restored the full dullness of the day. Meanwhile, the locals put on glasses with filtered lenses and viewed their homes in the colours of their choosing.

The next morning, the uplighters were secretly refitted with ultraviolet bulbs. Now, officials inspect the scheme by day, approving its neutral tones. Then, at night, goggle-eyed residents emerge to drink in forbidden colours, and an ecstasy of insects swarms to impossible flowers.

Schemes of Misconstruction (3)

[——] is a scheme of knock-throughs.

The floors, walls, skirtings, doors, sockets, meters, boilers, and pipes were installed with all the precision of a space mission, and the residents warned that any structural alteration, however small, was prohibited: to fit even a dimmer switch was forbidden, because their homes were already appointed for optimal living.

However, life rarely stays on script. A flapping hatch in a scullery wall was discreetly papered over in the interests of domestic peace; a light fitting repositioned to reduce the glare on a TV screen; and a wall removed to let in more light and chase away the winter blues. The living scheme quickly assumed new forms to fit unanticipated purposes.

But each structural change subtly undermined the scheme's carefully crafted social cohesion. Without its hatch, the scullery became a lonely, oppressive place; with an unhindered view of the hypnotic TV screen, weekends were wasted languishing on the couch; and long, summer months in an over-exposed bedroom brought the agony of insomnia.

As small changes in the physical environment accumulated, they sent ripples of lethargy and disconnect through the community, weakening the bonds between neighbours. This gave rise to more changes in the built environment. Peepholes were drilled through pensioners' doors, gardens were ripped up to keep cars close, metal shutters covered shop windows, bollards dead-ended streets.

Then one day, two adjoining semis were bought by a local businessman. He decided to knock his new homes together. As hammers crashed through plaster and brick, original fittings, fixtures – and ideals – were pulverised. But the owner was so pleased with the result, he did it again, and again.

Moving discreetly between his joined-up properties, he was able to conduct his business in person while keeping his exact whereabouts unknown. This gave him a competitive advantage within his field, enabling him to buy up ever more ex-council houses, until he owned swathes of the scheme, linking them up as he went. Next, he added conservatories and garages to his network, connecting street to street, until the whole scheme looked like an enormous rabbit run.

Some claim the visionary who drew up [——] so despaired of this desecration that he was driven to madness. Others say he was reconciled to the changes, accepting that deviation from the ideal lies deep within the knap of the planner's blank velum, and is written in tiny twitches of the pencil.

Mark slips in through an open door; McCann's upturned chair lies among scattered boxes.

'Lookin fur me?' The voice is distant and thin. It comes from a pyramid of boxes that reaches up to the roof. McCann stands at the top, his head swallowed by a hole. 'Mon up.'

Tentatively, Mark climbs onto the first box. It seems solid enough, so he stands and begins making his way towards the ceiling. As he scrambles from box to box, his hands and clothes are dusted with fine white powder.

'Somehin's in the wind,' McCann says, ducking inside as Mark reaches the top.

McCann's eyes are lit, his face flushed. He places a hand on Mark's neck, guiding him down, then up through the ragged hole in the corrugated iron. Gusts tousle Mark's hair, blowing it into his face. Through streaming eyes, he scans the scheme below.

'Whit dae ye see?' McCann asks.

Mark locates the garden he played in until the day he left, and the tree by the washing green he sat in every summer. It looks much bigger now, even with the lower branches pruned back, but his old primary school seems to have shrunk. The church hall, still whitewashed, is as clean as ever.

'Foodbanks aw oer the shop,' McCann growls. 'Canny be them, they're just free shoaps. 5G Phone masts? No chance. Plastic in the wattur? Shite music? Whit's chinged? How's nae cunt touchin ma gear?'

Mark's view tilts and his palms start to sweat - he feels nauseous. As the scene dims, a steadying paw grips his shoulder and he closes his eyes. When he reopens them, the streetlights are on. The world beyond the scheme has turned on its side, the city's edge curving away like the outer arm of *a vast galaxy, each scheme along its length a cluster of stars.*

'Are these the same schemes... the ones I visited? I don't recognise—'

'Don't look too hard. If ye stare full oan they disappear. Schemes urny built tae be gauked at.'

'I see them best when I don't try too hard.'

'Whit dae ye see noo?'

Mark follows the great wheel upwards. 'One day you're sitting in a tree, and the next – I think I'm going to throw up.'

McCann grips Mark by the neck and leads him back inside. Once upright, Mark focusses on a flickering strip light in front of his face. Piles of desiccated insects darken its corners.

'The day after his funeral—'

'Ye hid tae disappear, yer maw anoll.'

'I used to wonder why kids wouldn't play with me. Said they weren't allowed. When I went over the pitches, some of them wouldn't even look at me, never mind pass me the ball.'

'The Invisible Boy who did a vanishin act. Whit like wiz it through there?'

'At boarding school? Much the same. When I first arrived, I heard rumours about what happens to new boys, but nothing ever did. Not even after lights out. I started to think I must be a ghost.'

'Invisibility's a superpower. It kin protect ye fae anyhin.'

Mark ducks down and pops his head back out of the hole. A sheet of thin, low cloud covers the Sleeping Giant. In the moonlight, he looks like a shrouded corpse, his long, lifeless legs stretching away into the night.

6

'Hear that?'

McCann's open palm is poised in front of Mark's face. From somewhere deep inside the scheme comes the pitiful moan of a bus dragging itself uphill. The grimy lines in McCann's hand remind Mark of a map he once saw of the city's lost bus routes.

'Used tae be some buzz jumpin oan a bus, best laugh we ever hid. Gettin oot that scheme felt lit a prison brek.'

'Didn't Margaret Thatcher say around then that anyone who finds themselves on a bus after the age of twenty-five is a failure?'

'I'm talkin aboot when we wur just boys. That bus took us tae new places.'

'Yes, deregulation of the routes had a huge impact. Some claimed it would encourage people to stand on their own two feet, by which I suppose they meant sit in a car, while others said it would fleece people stranded in the schemes.'

'Build hooses in the back a beyond then haun the ony escape route tae a bunch a robbin cunts. Fuckin genius.'

'The ultimate captive market you might say.'

'Well me an yer da, we wur lit Robin Hoods aboot here when it came tae the buses.'

'So did you, er, 'tax' the operators and plough the proceeds back into the community?'

'Sorta. There wiz this wee dick Frankie, right. He wiz rakin it in oan the buses. Hid the punters stitched right up, emptyin their poakets every day. But aw we needed tae sort him oot wiz a shift sheet.'

'A what?'

'A drivers' timetable, so we knew who wiz gaun aff shift next.'

'Oh. So you could hold up this Frank guy on his way to the bank?'

'We smashed his heid in aboot a hunner times.'

McCann takes a crowbar from behind his seat and drops it onto the desk. Mark gasps.

'Frankie wiz a cartoon character remindin passengers tae gie the right money. 'Frankie Fast Fare.' His coupon wiz oan the fares boax in every bus in the city. Didny matter how many times we bashed him in, the wee shite just kept grinnin. Aw we hid tae dae wiz work oot whit bus wiz headin in tae the depot next, cos oan the last run fae the terminus the boax wiz burstin. Nae point tannin an empty is there?'

'Is this around the time you and dad started branching out with the cafe?'

'Aye. The buses took us right oot the scheme. Seed money. Funny int it. Seein how a ended up ownin hauf the city's bus routes.'

[——] is a scheme of ice.

On the edge of the city, there is a huge drumlin. Its peak is the city's highest point. Halfway up its steep, north face, you descend into a deep hole. The walls of this cavernous depression are curved and smooth and, at the bottom, lies a scheme.

Topography conspires to keep its streets in shadow all year round; they never feel the sun's touch. The winter's first snow lands on top of last year's, which by then has been trampled to dirty ice. Each fresh blanket is tramped down in turn, then buried by the winter that follows.

[——]'s central square is dominated by a large monument. Its plaque is entombed in frost, so the inscription has never been read. Its ice-encrusted limbs hang heavy with hoar, obscuring its original shape, so the intended tribute is unclear.

Some insist it's a war memorial, and predates the scheme, commemorating an extreme training exercise undertaken in the area by special troops. Others believe it's a Celtic Cross, perhaps erected to revere the consecrated ground of a long-lost churchyard. A few suggest the monument is older still, and marks blood spilt on the drumlin in an ancient battle between obscure factions in some forgotten squabble.

However, for all [——]'s people, the monument has come to symbolise the missing part of the drumlin, a mass of moraine that was gouged out by scouring ice, making space for the scheme to exist – a space they fill with their lives.

Once a year, the residents gather at their enigmatic monument to marvel at its newest crystalline spurs, and wonder quietly about its original meaning. Then they disperse, falling away like meltwater, coursing through narrow lanes and side streets. As they go, the people are momentarily warmed: by their neighbours' body heat, by the crunching impact of feet on snow, by the faint glow of the deep past.

Each returns home to light the fireplace and look up at the sky. The scheme has never seen the sun, but has never known true darkness either, because tiny ice crystals in the air scatter light everywhere.

[——] is a scheme of mirrors.

It has one street: a long, straight gully between opposing blocks of four-storey tenements. As you walk from end to end, you notice the flats on each side match up close to close, veranda to veranda, chimney to chimney. The walls are grey roughcast, the sort that darkens quickly in the rain and glimmers in the sun.

Where the street comes to a dead end, a red brick arch leaps across the road. This architectural flourish elegantly connects the scheme's twin halves and frames a huge doorway, the mouth of an iron and steel works.

Girders were once sent out through the arch to prop up imperial ambition. The works' fine iron filigree still garnishes distant palaces, but the building's glazed brickwork is cracked and dull, and colonised by mosses; its broken windows sprout shrubs.

The factory held on long enough to see the new scheme spring up by its entrance, which gave rise to a daily spectacle that is still recalled today: every morning, a long flatbed lorry would rumble along the road, each tiny bump in the tarmac sending a clatter bouncing off the tenement walls. This brought people out to watch the vehicle being inched towards the open arch, its precious load attended by crowbar-wielding chaperons, who fussed over it like bridesmaids on the way up the aisle.

As the lorry passed by, the onlookers fell silent, as if hypnotised. The cargo, a wedge of elongated stainless-steel sheets stacked on edge, held a mirror up to the scheme. Men would flatten lapels and straighten ties; senior ladies fussed with headscarves; mums slapped down the unruly fringes of children as they made faces at their friends; teenagers pretended to look away while swapping secret glances. In the gigantic silver screen, everyone had the picture's lead role. For a few seconds, regardless of how you might be cast for the rest of the day, you were a star: the central character, surrounded by a supporting ensemble of family, friends, and neighbours.

Now the arch at the end of the road hangs over corrugated shutters jammed shut by rust. As you walk away, you notice cracks in the scheme's symmetry: a boarded-up window, a garden fence flattened by a car, blue gloss paint in the gutter.

Those who tread these pavements keep their heads bowed; they only ever glimpse themselves in puddles. But these give an odd perspective – you stand alone against an empty sky, in a world turned upside down.

Schemes of Misconstruction (4)

[——] is a scheme of poltergeists.

Up on the surrounding hills, it looks tranquil, a suntrap sheltered from the prevailing wind, which is held high above the rooftops by the lie of the land.

But as you take the road in, an unquiet spirit makes itself heard. From a distance, it sounds like the wail of an injured animal. Then, down on the streets, you hear moans, groans, whistles, whispers; bus shelters buckle and flex; plastic bottles tom-tom along; battered cans clatter and clang; crisp-pokes scratch at the tarmac.

The scheme looks as chaotic as it sounds: rustic chalets rub shoulders with squat tenements; steel prefabs flank spherical polymer-clad eco-pods; genteel terraced rows with mock Tudor flourishes face down brutal concrete monoliths; brilliant, whitewashed surfaces are banded by glinting metal strips; dark wood extrudes from pebble dash – even the cement is multi-toned.

This clash of colours, textures, and materials creates a curious effect. In the morning sun, temperature differences arise from the materials' varying capacities for absorption and reflectivity, so micro-breezes waft over walls, doors, windows, and tiles. Some components hold the heat, creating hotspots, while others focus energy elsewhere, accelerating airflows and whipping up vortices.

By afternoon, thermals rise up, only to be pushed back down by the overhead winds. With nowhere else to go, the agitated air currents race down narrow lanes and squeeze between buildings.

Now as enduring as Jupiter's red spot, a storm rages through the scheme. Its terrorised residents rarely leave their homes, cowering in cupboards and cellars while doors and windows, letterboxes, cat flaps, vents, chimneys, and gutters rattle and shudder, as though gripped by malign intent.

As the poltergeists hurl plant pots, flatten fences, snap trees, and wreck street lights, teams of researchers study them, seeking ways to divert their destructive energy to better use. But uproar rages on as, bit by bit, the scheme falls apart: only when it is completely destroyed will its uneasy spirits find peace.

[——] is haunted by a restlessness that was summoned up in its original plans – but no-one understood this until it was too late.

[——] is a scheme of sidies.

You make your way down a steep lane through staggered tiers of tenements. At the bottom, the path opens out onto a flat space, strewn with red ash.

You emerge on the sidelines of a football match. No two players wear the same strip, but after watching for a few minutes, the flow of the game reveals two teams, their formations, and tactics.

The ball rolls to your feet and you're beckoned onto the pitch by a nearby player: you step out onto the gritty ash, nudging the ball along with you. You feel a lumbering presence bear down on you from behind: ahead is a blur of faces and colours, yet somehow, in an instant, you know who's on your side. You kick the ball upfield, and your peching stalker recedes.

With jackets for goalposts, a dispute soon arises over a shot at goal. The players bicker, some referring to previous unresolved incidents, while others counter with their own grievances. The goalkeeper launches the ball into the sky, and in the time it takes to rise and fall, grudges are forgotten and attention returns to the game.

This lasts until the next goalmouth incident, when another round of squabbling breaks out, with competing versions of the scoreline barked from all corners of the pitch. The wildly differing claims suggest that each player keeps score only from when they themselves arrived on the pitch. It's clear that while chasing the same ball, everyone is playing in a different match with its own defining moments of triumph and disaster, glory and ignominy.

Locals say the game, known simply as The Sidey, has endured at the heart of the scheme for as long as anyone can remember. Some claim it began as a kickabout between tradesmen and local youths to celebrate the completion of the last tenement, and when the workers left for the pub, the lads played on. They say that somewhere deep under the jumbled goalposts lie the forgotten, dusty overalls of the men who started it.

The relentless pace of the game takes its toll, exhausted players occasionally walking off the pitch to disappear back up the lane. But as quickly as one player leaves, another joins. Some time after your arrival, you notice fresher, faster players around you. If you play long enough, you'll find that no-one on the pitch was here when you arrived.

Those who live close by have stepped on and off the pitch more times than they can remember; shooting at one goal, then the other; sometimes with, and sometimes against, friends and relatives. But with no referee, no final whistle ever sounds, and no winning goal is ever scored.

As night arrives, the eternal sidey rages on, the fluorescent strips of a thousand sculleries illuminating the pitch like floodlights on a giants' terracing.

Schemes of Transport (4)

[——] is a scheme of bus shelters.

It used to be a test ground for new designs, the residents rating them for comfort and durability. Some shelters had sleek chrome interiors, or plush reclining seats. A few were fitted with heaters; one even boasted an upper deck with a spiral exit chute.

These were developed at a nearby industrial unit, which held every type of shelter: from the antique, cast iron model to the later steel box, and the short-lived Perspex hamster cage right up to modern, continental, semi-open, shatter-proof glass. Reflecting the changing times, each type was proofed against a different adversary: weather, graffiti, fire, general rage. Deep in the unit's vaults, there even survived an old Anderson Shelter, adapted for reuse during the post-deregulation Route Wars. For decades, this is where the city's damaged shelters were brought for repair.

Due to the high attrition rate, the workshop expanded over the years, growing into a vast hangar. Meanwhile, the local housing stock fell into decline until it was deemed beyond repair, so the city's wrecking crews moved in and began opening up gaps across the scheme.

With a rebuilding programme mooted, the displaced residents were offered temporary accommodation on the other side of the city, which, given the state of the local bus service, many felt was as good as exile. So people made their own arrangements instead, some simply choosing to slip away in the night. With the sudden disappearance of a large number of tenants, the rebuilding plans were put on hold and the demolitions stepped up.

Soon there were no homes left, and the buses stopped

running to [——]. Yet by now the scheme was served by more bus shelters than ever; they were crammed onto every spare inch of pavement, even on the off-route back streets.

It later emerged that as the houses came down, the workshop was being quietly emptied of its stock and the scheme rebuilt' as a shanty town of bus shelters.

If you walk to [——] today, where the houses used to be, you'll find trees and scrub. But along the pavements stand rows of comfortable, well appointed, weather-tight dwellings. No-one asks the residents' opinions anymore, but if you did, they'd tell you that bus shelters make perfect homes for council tenants, because they're designed to be occupied for an indefinite period of time while enduring endless broken promises.

With their lives permanently on hold, the residents have mastered the art of waiting; [——] is a scheme of infinite patience, located beyond disappointment.

'There's something I'd like to ask.'

McCann is slumped low in his chair, a dog lead wrapped round his wrist like chain mail. He turns it, watching the light slip over its surfaces. His eyes swivel towards Mark. 'Mon stretch yer legs.'

With a low whine, Mark's chair scrapes the concrete. McCann, gripping his upper arm, leads him towards the mountain of cardboard boxes looming at the far end of the unit. As they weave through scattered piles of boxes, the dog chain rattles in McCann's hand. The further in they go, the colder the air feels on Mark's face.

'Yer wonderin whit's in they boxes,' McCann says, casually flicking one with the chain on his way past. A plume of dust wafts over them, catching Mark's throat. 'It's no the usual gear.'

'Er, it was actually, ahem, about my fees.'

Mark's face starts to tingle. He hears gurgling; a stream of orange water is running down the wall. It has begun to seep out across the floor and, in the corner, it forms a pool. As they splash through it, dark residue stains their shoes.

'Ironstone,' McCann says.

'Right—'

'Oozes up oot the grun.'

'I see—' Mark's thoughts are running away, zipping around his head, half formed ideas, too fluid, words melding – he fishes for his tongue – it's adrift, like a dropped oar. He remembers elocution lessons, takes a slow breath, and starts again: 'Six years...at school...and four...at Oxford...so ten years. The fees...private tutors...mum said dad's insurance...paid them.'

'Yer da wiz always wan step ahead.'

'But I've checked, Dad didn't have one...a life insurance

policy. So...where did the money come from?'

'Ye did economics aye?'

'Er...a little.'

'Well ye should know better than tae ask where money comes fae. That's the whole point a money, naebody knows where it comes fae, or where it's gaun.' He nudges Mark in the ribs, sending him around a box he was about to walk into.

'Ah! But someone... must have taken care of things.'

'An if ye've got enough ae it ye can stiy invisible yer whole life. Hink yer colleges an schools gie a fuck where their fees come fae?'

McCann brings them to a halt at the base of the box mountain. Mark feels the chill coming from it. His legs wobble, forcing him to lean on it.

'But something... doesn't add up—'

'Nothin adds up wi money. It can bend light, make hings disappear, pit them where they urny.'

Mark notices the boxes at his feet are sitting in water and have started to buckle. Overhead, some have split open and are leaking a dark resin, forming stalactites.

'But there's no policy, so how, so who—'

'This place has done somehin tae it. The air, the damp, fuck knows, but somehin's chainged it.'

At the far end of the puddle, Mark notices a layer of green algae. Even at a distance it smells poisonous, making his sinuses throb. In places, the garish slime has climbed onto the boxes, carpeting them, making the cardboard mountain look like a natural formation. On the edge of his vision, Mark senses something flitting between the boxes – a jumble of hands and feet – then something passes through him. It feels like a shadow within his ribs. McCann is close.

'Yer maw still thinks yer auld man hid a policy. But that widda caused too minny problems. A paid yer fees.'

Mark turns to face McCann. 'But why?'

'Cos ee asked us tae.'

7

McCann blows smoke at the hole in the roof. His legs, crossed at the ankles, stretch out across the desk. Between his knees, a flick knife stands embedded in the wood. Through the smoke, Mark sees, in the tread of his uncle's Timberland boots, the rooftops of a scheme laid out in hexagonal blocks – a honeycomb metropolis of bees, deep in the sleep of an endless winter.

McCann jerks upright, plucking the knife from the wood. He reaches under his seat and lifts a parcel onto the desk; he slits it open and a pool of blood runs into the wood.

'Steaks?' Mark guesses hopefully, peering through the grease paper at the glistening flesh within. McCann stands, wielding a hammer.

'Prime cuts,' he says, spreading them on the desk.

THUD! He brings the hammer down, spattering the desk and surrounding floor, then heaves out his words between blows: 'Right tae Buy'—THUD! 'Best hing they ever did'—THUD!

His face already spotted, Mark feels a fleck of gristle land on his bottom lip. He resists the urge to wipe it.

'A total game chainger—' THUD! 'We bought oors before any cunt aboot here hid their application in—' THUD! 'We wur even in front a the cooncillors—' THUD! 'Wisny long before we owned hauf the scheme—' THUD! 'Then we startit buyin up every hoose oan the market—' THUD! 'Good auld Maggie!'

THUD! THUD! THUD!

Mark doesn't flinch at this final salvo. Instead, he follows the aftershock of the last blow up through his uncle's arm, across his shoulder, into his neck and face; McCann's distorted features oscillate comically before settling back into their familiar arrangement.

'Hear that?' McCann asks, smoothing his red-speckled Fred Perry.

'What?'

'That fuckin bangin.' He waves the hammer around his head, then resumes his pounding on the other slab of meat, this time following the beat in his head.

THUD!

'The auld property gemme—' THUD! 'Aye been legit—' THUD! 'Respectable—' THUD! 'Nae bank or lender—' THUD! 'Argues wi rateable value.'

He drops the hammer on the floor.

'Who came up wi it? 'Right tae Buy'?'

For the first time, Mark notices the carnage in front of his face; fibrous strands strewn across the desk, some hanging over the edges.

'Er, well, in a sense 'Right to Buy' was about selling you something you already owned, a bit like flogging off library books. The real aim was to obliterate the principle of common ownership. Several right leaning think tanks floated it around the same time, so I suppose you might say 'Right to Buy' was in the aether.'

'Fuckin right it wiz. An it didny stoap wi hooses. Drugs. Boadies. Souls.' McCann surveys the bloody mess before him. 'Whit am a like? Ma boay prefers it this wiy.' He gathers the scraps back into the shredded parcel and hands it to Mark. 'Stick that ootside fur us, eh?'

Schemes of Aesthetics (4)

[——] is a scheme of facades.

The city's finest draughtsmen, masons, and roofers were commissioned by the Planning Department to set a sparkling jewel in the council's crown of schemes – and so [——] was erected as a tribute to civic imagination.

Its breathtaking central avenue remains one of the wonders of the city. Its terraced rows might have been shipped from Timbuktu, its semis lifted from the suburbs of Arcadia, its cottages plucked from the pages of Andersen. Glazed brickwork dazzles, every front door the threshold to a happy union between architectural styles hitherto thought incompatible. Wrought iron awnings drip with Mackintosh, columns ooze Thomson, and every feature beckons the eye to prismatic bay windows depicting miracles of social engineering in leaded glass.

Word of this spectacular achievement soon spread, and people began arriving from all over the city simply to walk the scheme's boulevards and imbibe its magic. Each pilgrim finds their own reward: the depressed are uplifted, the emphysematous breathe easier, the sciatic stand tall once more.

But for all its allure, no-one ever talks of moving here. So much money was poured into these fabulous frontages that by the time they were finished there was no money left for anything else. So the houses have no side or back walls; there are no interiors; roofs stop at the apex.

A peek behind the famous front elevations reveals nothing but crude wooden buttresses groaning under their burden, though some have plastic sheets draped over them to accommodate sleeping bags.

Those who come to admire prefer not to think of what lies behind the facades, so it is never discussed; only oohs and aahs escape their lips.

But everyone knows the truth. Indistinct forms are glimpsed behind the coloured glass – the weather-beaten faces of [——]. They peer up and down the avenues, as if waiting for someone to come back and finish the job.

[——] is a scheme of mines.

The area is dotted with ancient collieries. Many were opened, worked, and closed long before record-keeping became an industry requirement, so the precise whereabouts of their disused shafts and drifts are unknown.

During a long dry spell, or after heavy rain, or a sudden thaw, or when hidden forces rebalance deep within the earth, sinkholes open up in the middle of the scheme. It's impossible to guess exactly where the next one will appear. A wheelie bin might suddenly be taken, or a bus shelter, a garden shed, a nursery school annexe, a row of shops, a church hall, the library, the old folks home – or even a whole football pitch.

You might be unsettled by the possibility that, at any moment, uncharted history could come crashing into your day. You'd maybe feel uneasy walking on pavements where each step invites unfathomable disaster. Surely, you would think, on ground so exhausted, where every second is menaced by the past, that nothing could inspire hope, because nothing can be expected to last – a brick wall, a relationship, a stroll in the park.

But where past and future are two sides of the same lost coin, people have no choice but to live but in the moment, so no-one complains about the routine disasters, or even acknowledges them. There is no public mourning, nor does anyone joke about their losses.

There's a locally held belief that because the holes take from the descendants of those who dug them, what they claim shouldn't be grudged. Some even write off their misfortunes – a vanished conservatory, a collapsed driveway, a disappeared dog – as offerings to the past, a form of tribute to the processes that carved out the world in which we live.

The cave-ins are never reported to the authorities, so are never investigated or highlighted in the press. Occasionally, a whisper of some mishap will escape the scheme and swirl round a news desk floor, but where obscure, distant schemes are concerned, the papers and TV stations are riddled with their own gaping blind spots, so the story always vanishes without trace.

The last mine was abandoned after a fire. Down the local pub, they say it was never properly extinguished, that in deep pockets it smoulders still, slowly consuming the city.

[——] is a scheme of visitors.

No-one mentions its name in polite circles, or would even admit to knowing it, but after dark, taxis from all over the city slip in, glide through its backstreets, and roll gently to a stop.

Tonight, an engine chuckles to itself as a passenger fights his way out of his seat and, blinking through a fog of alcohol, spills onto the street. Once on his feet, he finds his mark. Familiar cracks in the pavement run under his shoes. Each visitor knows their drop spot intimately, yet were they brought to a point even a few metres away, they'd be lost.

He feels his way up the close, fingering the usual grooves and bumps. His face is known far beyond the scheme from thousands of television appearances, the latest of which is on a repeats channel being watched in the flat he is staggering past. He pauses at the door, feeling somehow accused by a long-lost splinter of himself, then presses on.

At the top, he takes a breath and raps on the door with the side of his fist, mimicking the jaunty authoritarian rhythm of the police. But his is an empty threat, because his knock is as familiar here as his craggy face.

As he waits, his muttering echoes down the stairwell. But he needn't worry about being overheard, his being here is no problem. In this scheme, celebrity assures anonymity; people live out their days hiding in plain sight, and everybody knows that those who knock on doors are soon no longer themselves.

In the next close, a newsreader stands on the same spot. In the close beyond, a celebrated lawyer. After that there's a pop star, then an MP. The doors open, and business is done; the visitors waft back to their waiting chariots, and depart.

[——] is a labyrinth within which you can only cross your own path, because everyone has their own way in and out.

[——] is a scheme of silence.

The world's first anechoic housing scheme was praised as a unique feat of structural and social engineering. Thanks to its ingenious design, raucous music never gets into the wrong ears; late night TV viewers are never sent scrambling for the remote by the dreaded rap on the wall; and DIY fanatics are free to hammer, drill, and saw with abandon.

Eggbox-shaped structures cover every inch of wall, door, window, roof, pole, bus shelter, and tree. Even the pavements and roads are studded with tiny rubber rhomboids that massage walkers' feet, stealing away the sound of footfall while soothing the subject into quiet contentment.

The natural noise of the outdoors – rain, wind, and hail – is also on mute, because the streets and gable ends are carefully angled to funnel away turbulent air, ensuring that the residents remain undisturbed.

The scheme's uniquely flat soundscape unsettles the unaccustomed visitor, but those born to it have adjusted their habits and ways of thinking. Conversations are always confidential, because you have to get close up to be heard. But even when head-to-head, your words might still be smuggled away by a nearby wall or snapped up by a passing padded dog.

Such is the effort involved in having a normal conversation in this auditory desert that, over time, people have come to prefer talking to themselves. If they bother to articulate at all, they do so in a unique verbal shorthand that can only be understood by the speaker, so the scheme is home to a population of rapidly diverging personal languages that, with each passing day, grow ever more mutually unintelligible.

The human voice, in a losing battle with internal monologues that make most sense when left unspoken, is vanishingly rare. Older residents choose instead to drift quietly in their thoughts, rewinding and replaying past conversations, arguments, singsongs, laughs.

Meanwhile, in [——]'s playgrounds and parks, children spend every waking moment running, leaping, skipping, rolling, crashing through the silence.

There's a scheme made of pixels. You've probably seen it, nearly everyone has. It first turned up on a webpage where nostalgic images of days gone by are posted and discussed.

One such photograph, attributed to the city's Planning Department, whipped up a firestorm of debate and a blitz of reposts, likes, loves, laughs, cares, and wows.

The anonymous poster didn't say when the photo was taken, but countless guesses were made based on the quality of the camera, its handling of light, darkness, and shade.

There were more clues in the types of houses depicted; the condition of the gardens; the health and thickness of the hedges and grass; the state of the walls; the type of fences; the number of cars parked on the road; the style of the curtains, blinds, and window frames; a sliver of wallpaper seen through a window; the clothes, hairstyles, and demeanour of the children. Any of these might place the picture at a particular moment in time, but on the discussion thread, no-one could agree on exactly when that was.

Furthermore, based on the shape of a roof, the camber of a road, the angle of a bend, the lean of a pole, a chipped kerbstone, the scar on a girl's brow, each viewer saw in the photo a different scheme. Each would recall a different street and recognise a different classmate, so arguments raged, not only about when it was taken, but where.

Given the huge interest it has generated, some have concluded that the photo is fake, posted by a troll to provoke conflict. Or maybe it's a collage of different images created with the best of intentions, to bring people together in the act of remembering. It might even portray a real street that was built and populated just to showcase all the elements of scheme life which, immediately after the picture was taken, was evacuated and bulldozed.

If you haven't seen it yet and search for it online, you won't find it. But when the time is right, it will find you. On that day, you will go on a journey to the scheme inside you heart, which lies somewhere within a vast city containing all possible schemes. Small bits of that great city come tumbling through the clouds in the form of memories. They land on top of each other, making a jumbled mountain of words; you'll find them lying at the bottom of your screen, like a pile of broken bricks propping up the picture.

'That last time we spoke–'

'Efter the funeral? It was aw sortit long before then. Ye were gaun at the end ae the summer anyway. Whit happened way yir da only broat it forward a few weeks.'

A loud bang sends Mark swivelling towards the door; he's relieved to see it swinging in the wind. McCann, no longer hostage to such reflexes, watches Mark, waiting for him to settle back into his seat.

'When they come they come. Mere a'l show ye sumhin.'

McCann breenges out of his seat towards the open door. Mark rises hesitantly as McCann ducks out into the alley at the back of the unit. Rushing to catch up, Mark stumbles, half tripping out the door. As he flaps at thin air, he's blinded by a low sun, and a black cloud engulfs his face. He swats it away: a swarm of flies that had been feasting on the putrefied meat on the ground.

'Two days no touched. Know whit that means?' McCann asks, glancing up and down the alley, before striding off into the sun. His boots crunch on sandstone chips. 'They're already here!'

By the time Mark catches up, McCann is staring out at the hills; the Sleeping Giant bathes in golden light.

'Look efter im ya big prick, eh,' McCann mutters, before brushing past Mark on his way back up the alley. He spins back, gesturing for Mark to be still. 'Feel that?'

Mark looks down at his shoes, still slowly settling into the loose pink stones. He detects something: a shudder in the ground, but so faint he thinks he imagined it. Then he feels it again, and again. 'What is it?'

'Ma ma used tae say when the Giant took in a new heart he'd let ye hear it wan last time.'

'I remember mum telling me that. She said it was the Giant saying thanks for sending...whoever.'

'Thanks? Ee owes me a big fuckin dunt then.'

McCann recalls the hills under a different sky – in midwinter, empty of stars. Where the road stops, he gets out and climbs, burns chortling at his every slip; he digs down into the darkness; the rain is relentless; the burns get louder, until the roar of crashing water is all there is; he skids back down and opens the boot.

'So dad wanted me to go? And mum?'

'Look at im, lyin there prayin.'

'For what?'

'Rain. Tae hammer im intae the grun tae it washes im away.'

8

'It took me a while to get used to the new name thing.'

'Yer auld granny's name. Came in handy.'

'For about half a term I didn't react when it was called. The teachers thought I was thick.'

'Ye wur hamesick.'

'I didn't have a home anymore. Or anything else. To lose everything, including your parents, is one thing; but to lose your name too, that's, like, well, it feels like you've been erased.'

'Ye don't hiv a name in this gemme. Well no wan embdy'll say, ye never know who's recordin.'

'But everyone knows you. Your name's legendary around here.'

'Exactly, it's ma name they know. That hing's fuck aw tae dae wi me. It floats aboot here hauntin the place. A just staun behine it when it suits me.'

A glimmer on the wall catches McCann's eye. A fluorescent tube swings gently on a rusty chain, under it a square patch of wall whiter than the rest. Around its edges, gathered grime outlines some long gone sign. A safety notice maybe, or fire drill instructions.

'Mibbae it's me daen the hauntin. When a need tae be somebdy a pull oan an alias. It's like pittin oan a new jaikit. Ye should never trust the cover,' he grunts, lifting a large box up onto the desk. On it, there's a picture of a television surrounded by Chinese characters. 'Yer maw hud nae choice. She hid tae get oot the road, an we hid tae get you away an all. If we hidny ye widny be sittin here moanin aboot it.' He slaps the box. 'Talkin aboot new names, whit'll we call this stuff? It needs rebrandin.'

McCann hears a soft tinkling sound – he thinks of loose change flowing into a rucksack – and spots a new leak, water running down the wall onto the floor. On the way down, it clings to the bricks like a protruding vein, throbbing with uneven flow. He always thought money behaved like water, pooling in the lowest places; but Mark's reports chart shifting ground, a warped landscape riddled with fissures. Now a stranger in his own empire, he can no longer read the maps. He scoops up a bag of powder from the box and weighs it in his hand.

'It wiz sound when it came in, but noo...shoulda goat you tae dae a wee chemistry class anoll.'

'Er, I don't think my brain could withstand another discipline.'

'You could dae anyhin, yev goat yer da's brain. Law, medicine, pharmacology. Whit made ye go fur the social policy stuff anywiy?'

'I dunno, it seemed that PPPs, PPIs and so on were going to be the next big thing. Transformational. There was talk of investment coming down the track on a scale not seen in decades.'

'Aye.'

'Looking back, my advisor of studies played a big part in interesting me in those areas.'

'Am sure Professor Thomson gave ye a right good steer.'

'Profess— what, you know him?'

'Uch a know everybdy.'

Schemes of Bureaucracy (4)

[——] is a scheme of graves.

Its long streets stretch out like the fingers of a lover's hand reaching across a table. But they only ever meet the cold clasp of the dead, because each road is flanked, on both sides, by a strip of land reserved for burials.

This unusual arrangement arose after the builders began work, but were then ordered to stop. Discussions with a neighbouring local authority about extending the city boundary had floundered on the ambiguity of an ancient feu, so the half-finished scheme was placed in limbo.

The completed units sat on land earmarked by the other council for the expansion of a nearby graveyard, but since housing shortages plagued both worlds, a compromise was reached: the two realms would share the land, each street for the living alternating with one for the deceased.

Here, it is impossible to separate life from death. From bedrooms in terraced rows, domestic arguments spill out of open windows, rebound off gravestones, and come back as ghostly echoes, like reprimands from the dead, to interrupt the quarrellers.

Children's playful screeches animate back gardens, pricking the ears of mossy cherubs, who smile over fences as though hoping to join in: stopping the games dead.

On double-parked roads, impatient taxi drivers honk emphatically, as if trying to rouse the dead; then a passenger will clamber aboard whose complexion and demeanour makes it impossible to tell from which side of the divide they've come.

Some residents say they're content beside such quiet neighbours, under the watch of alabaster angels; while others insist they cannot rest easy beneath the daily, scything shadow of the Celtic cross.

What none say out loud is that there is no peace here, not even deep in the night. If you listen carefully, somewhere on the scheme's edge tireless diggers turn the heavy, black earth and sift a disputed feu – but under whose authority, no-one ever dares ask.

[——] is a scheme of symphonies.

Its low, medium, and high-rise flats are arranged in concentric crescents, so from the central shopping circus, their layout resembles that of an orchestra. In the middle of the circus, a gently landscaped hill sets the whole ensemble around you as it might appear from a conductor's rostrum.

Beyond this staggered edifice, the sky peeks in from the wings and peers down from the gods, but it plays a key role. The stormy heavens' non-stop bellowing tantrums are modulated, retuned, and inflected by the scheme's vast concrete structures – in the spaces between buildings, around the water tanks on the roofs, through tiny crenulations in the cladding. These combine to channel a tumultuous, moaning westerly that has sustained its epic performance since the day the scheme was built.

Monolithic gable ends funnel the winds, imbuing them with subsonic moans; steel tanks flex and warp in the fluctuating air pressure, throwing out ominous booms; mosaics of holes left between ground floor breeze blocks wail shrill laments; whole buildings resonate on unearthly scales.

Listen more carefully and you can hear a sea breeze bluster over an ocean swell, gathering up the rage of the angry Atlantic as it races for land, holding itself tight while barrelling down the glens, before smashing into [——]'s vertical cliff walls. What you hear in this howling cacophony of wrath is the dying breath of an old song.

But the discerning listener might also pick out something else, and smile at the cheeky, subtle counterpoint playing sotto around the edges of the piece. From your central grassy podium, you catch glimpses of the in-house players, tiny silhouettes flitting between their gigantic instruments.

Stretching on tiptoe, arms bent backwards, slight frames arched, they produce delicate fluting notes. With jackets held taut over their heads, children catch the wind and ride the eddies. They make haunting harmonies, and give [——]'s wild ocean symphony its soul.

Schemes of Coercion (4)

[——] is a scheme of explosions.

A report recommended the scheme be razed and the land cleared of all traces of its existence. This would allow another scheme to be built in its place on a brand-new layout, with better housing, offering a higher quality of life.

But then a second council report highlighted an acute accommodation crisis across the city. This forced a rethink on the demolition of existing housing stock, so at the last moment, [——] was reprieved.

On site, where the big countdown was already underway, the clock was stopped on three. But with the scheme evacuated, fenced off, and impregnated with military grade high explosive, the residents couldn't simply be waved back to their homes. Every load bearing wall, strut, and pillar was wired up, as were places of learning and worship, shops, lampposts, benches, and a recently opened memorial garden. To ensure the scheme's total destruction, even its sprawling, undeveloped, grassy wastelands had been heavily mined.

The demolition squads were ordered back in to disarm and uplift their materials, but then a financial bomb exploded, with the contractor subject to a winding up order. Its directors were suspended, the workforce dismissed.

Another firm was appointed to come in and clear things up, but amid the confusion, all the site plans had been lost, so the new squad was forced to work blind – no-one knew where all the wires went.

When [——]'s people eventually returned home, their revised tenancy agreements included caveats. These mention that dampness degrades wiring; protective sheathing perishes in frost; bacteria attack organic compounds, which can cause endothermic reactions; vermin gnaw at everything.

Now people shut doors gently and speak softly; they're conservative in their choices of music and comedy – nothing too raucous or hilarious – and when stepping outside, they tread warily, tiptoeing as though through an avalanche zone, always aware that in this scheme your next step could be your last.

Every so often, a charge goes off. Some are taken in their sleep, or on the way back from the shops, or standing at a school crossing. But these incidents are considered part of life here, like hailstones and heart attacks.

Each of [——]'s hidden wires is an umbilical cord that infuses the scheme, not with life, but chaos, which is reborn over and over in random eruptions of heat, light, and noise.

[——] is a scheme of refraction.

Two buildings command the skyline. While the streets below present a drab collage of tired greys, the new builds at the top of the hill are made of honey-coloured bricks, and within their playfully landscaped grounds, walls meet roofs at jaunty angles.

The quirky twin structures were designed as a complementary pair to book-end community life; one is a primary school, and the other a care home for the elderly. Of their many shared features, the most striking is the windows. The classrooms' panes are tinted shades of purple and blue, the care home's an array of oranges and reds, and when the sun shines, it throws colours through the buildings.

Sometimes, as the home's residents settle down to their daily game of pre-lunch bingo, a cloud will shift, showering hands, faces, and tables in rubies, cherries, and scarlets. At that moment, the children next door, perhaps shedding skins of glue at a classroom sink, will find themselves splashing in inky, lilac puddles.

When the youngsters have had lunch, they run outside, squinting in the unfiltered light. Each day, one of them is picked by the others to sneak through a gap in the fence and spy on the home. Standing on tiptoe, they cup their hands to peach and cream windows and peer through the mottled glass.

It's impossible to make out any detail; time behaves differently on the other side, somehow moving fast and slow in the same moment. Indistinct limbs and faces pass like creatures swimming through a watery world. If you move your head from side to side, a clock on the far wall warps and dilates.

By late afternoon, the languid occupants of both buildings feel time weighing heavier. On one side, the residents bathe in the warmth of refracted sunlight as they slumber through bygone days of cerise, tangerine, and wine; while next door, a hushed game of heads-down-thumbs-up casts adrift tired young adventurers, their faces daubed purple and ultramarine as they set off for the deep recesses of space, or bob on the open seas.

Sometimes, glimpsed through a half-shut eyelid, a shape will appear at the window: an unkempt, white head of hair, which in the fanciful glass might be taken for a fluffy cloud fallen from the sky. Meanwhile, on the other side of the window, there's confusion in the mind of a young girl peering into a deep blue grotto. She blinks in the harsh light, unable to find her way back to the classroom she left just a few minutes ago, a lifetime ago.

In the refracted scheme, only those who walk the grey streets at the bottom of the hill can see the whole rainbow.

Schemes of Abandonment (4)

[——] is a scheme of quads.

Arriving here feels like turning up a week late for a party: everything has already happened, and everyone is gone.

Hedges that once raced children to the sky are uprooted; gardens that realised the bloom of a lifetime's labour, reclaimed by sedge; verandas that saw the hills turn to rust a thousand times at dusk, lost in blind space.

Even the litter has been outlasted by desolation; the indestructible crisp bags, cartons, cans, and wrappers were carried off and dumped elsewhere by some dreadful gyre.

The sketchy outlines of nameless streets still appear among mats of dock leaves and clumps of stunted gorse. Here and there among the mosses, cracked foundations mark the boundaries between invisible kitchens, living rooms, bedrooms, bathrooms, closes, larders.

A posse of quad bikers crosses the distant horizon. They buck and bounce on tufts of grass, career over crumbling kerbstones, dip down into covered potholes. Each rider wears a helmet and ski mask, as if to protect themselves from the erosion that assaults all who linger here.

As they wander through nothingness, their engines rasp like September wasps, irritated at forgetting why they came, where they wanted to go.

They vanish; for a moment the wind tastes of petrol. Then the thrum of engines dies, and there's nothing left: the world is a horseless steppe.

—steppe.

THUD!

Mark's last word arrives like a distant bomb blast, the full stop behind his final plosive a blow to the base of McCann's skull. The walls judder; puddles ripple; a loose light fitting squeaks.

THUDA-THUDA-THUDA-

Hands on desk, McCann pushes himself to his feet. 'Hear that? Piledriver's startit. Aboot fuckin time. If they don't get a move on the plant hire'll cost merr than the bastartin land.'

'I used to feed the newts slugs out by the back end. It was really swampy.'

'A drained it.'

'Wasn't it under some sort of protection, listed as a Site of Special Scientific Interest?'

'It's prime hoosebuildin land noo. Know the biggest cost in buildin? Broon envelopes. Land soaks up merr money than rain. But that oer there's fuck all, 32 flats, just a wee trial run. There's real contracts comin up.'

'The government's new 'Homes for All' initiative.'

'Mega tenders. Tens a thousands a units. Whole new housin associations, mixed developments, renovations tae, upgrades, hingwy whit dae they call it – future proofin. They're rebuildin every scheme in Scotland. New toons, hauf the greenbelt, an every scrag end a spare grun's up for grabs.' *He sits, and raps his drawer with his knuckles.* 'But the auld address book ony gets ye so for. That's where you come in.'

'Me? How?'

'Av goat a joab fur ye.'

'Doing what?'

'Just whit ye've been daen. Tellin stories.'

They both know that what McCann really needs is Mark's voice, his words: those grandiose grammatical constructions that inspire confidence and trust.

'Backed up wi due academic rigour of course,' McCann smirks.

Mark's heartbeat loses its rhythm, as if trying to sync with McCann's piledriver.

'Er, I'm not sure I'm the right—'

'Come on, you've seen hings in they schemes naebdy else wid. These clowns'll be eatin oot yer haun.'

'But I have an internship lined up. It's with this policy group, they do a lot of good stuff for—'

'Ye don't need some wanky think tank, ye've done yer apprenticeship wi me. A sent you oot there tae find somehin oot fur me, am still waitin fur an answer by the way, but a found oot somehin aboot you.'

'Me? What's that?'

'Ye kin sell a vision.'

Mark recalls a heavy wooden door swinging open on screaming hinges; his first day at the new school.

'So this would be what, a PR-slash-lobbying sort of thing?'

'Merr than that. You'll be the drivin force behind a dynamic young business, providin a public a service by...helpin...tae...' He tails off, inviting Mark to continue.

'Oh! Er, realise the transformative vision of the new housing paradigm.'

'Aw that shite. Look, relax, am no invitin ye intae ma world, a want intae yours. Av goat contacts in cooncils, agencies, Holyrood. A just need you tae take them fur walkies.' McCann launches the rubber chew bone across the desk; Mark catches it.

'An don't worry aboot yer ma, leave her tae me.'
THUDA-THUDA-THUD: the piledriver stops.
'Welcome tae the firm.'

9

'I know why it's not selling.'

McCann is transfixed by the mountain covering the unit's back wall, watching it grow before his eyes. Its black peak nudges the roof. In its twisted formations, he glimpses deformed fragments of forgotten faces: accusing eyes, slack jaws, flattened noses.

'It's the schemes,' Mark continues. 'There's no psychotropic bite point.'

Drooling lips protrude from a black escarpment, mocking McCann, as if poised to speak the truth he already knows; that all he has achieved is this grotesque edifice—

'They've reached maximum social entropy.'

—and that locked up in its solidifying mass is the thickening lifeblood of his empire, which should be flowing freely, running through the schemes, infusing his ventures: bloating profits, floating assets, carrying him off on a sea of credit—

'Even time no longer makes sense there.'

—enabling him to lubricate gears, unstick levers, turn the wheels of the world—

'Slow doon, am just a thick cunt fae the back end,' McCann says, tracing the latest bumps with his fingertips. The cold crawls over his hand. 'Whit aboot time?'

'Where each moment is invisible to the next, and severed from the last – where now is all there is – you can't offer an escape: there's nowhere to go. Those schemes you sent me to, they were built to hold people, but not time. The planners flattened the past, then the free market strangled the future.'

McCann presses his palms to the mountain, letting them numb. 'If life's this mental, whit merr kin drugs dae?'

'Exactly. Your business model only works within a structured society; it feeds off the degradation of order. Without structured time, if everything is just formless chaos, well...' Mark ruffles a patch of lichen in front of his face. 'But it's not just about time, it's space too. Those schemes—'

'Fuck the schemes, a'll shift it in the burbs. It's no too late, we'll fill their cavities wi free offers – Special Insulation – gie them a taster.'

'That won't work either. This stuff, whatever it is, can only deliver one hit.'

'Whit?' The chill crawls up McCann's arms.

'It's something to do with how it joins things up. Space, time, people. The very first time you opened one of those bags, what were you thinking about?'

'Fuck knows. Nothin.'

'Well I was thinking about this place, where I came from, what's happened since, and it seems to have started some sort of chain reaction. Now it's out there, everywhere. I think by talking about the schemes, and looking at them, really looking, and telling their stories, it's changed them.'

'How could that chainge them?'

'Well for one thing, they're no longer hermetically sealed.'

'Noo the bag's burst they're seepin in through the waws an up oot the grun.'

'You imposed your reality on the schemes for years. You stashed them away, hid them from themselves. But now a different story is being told.'

'So it wiz aw ma fault.'

'I wouldn't say that. You had lots of help.'

'Aw they schemes ye went tae—'

'I only visited one scheme. As I was trying to tell you, space is changing too. There only is one scheme out there, we just couldn't see it before.'

'We need tae get hings movin, start lobbyin, it's no too late if we— where ye gaun?'

As Mark walks away, McCann's eyes stay on the mountain.

'There are still some things I need to see.'

'We never gied it a name!' McCann shouts, pressing his cheek into a glassy hollow.

Mark turns at the door. 'How about Sleeping Giant?'

Schemes of Bureaucracy (5)

[——] is a scheme of computation.

As you skirt the surrounding marshes, you notice something curious: on three sides, the scheme has no windows. Every room, kitchen, toilet, and front door faces the same way, so all the houses bask in the sun until it dips behind a steep, grassy hill.

When the scheme was first built, council inspectors carrying clipboards would tramp up this hill at dusk, study the scene below though binoculars, and furiously scribble their findings.

On the same ridge today, a concrete stump, once a trigpoint, is now a stool for partying teenagers; their rusty cans lie scattered about your feet. But what makes this spot unique is that, from here, all the scheme's windows can be seen at once. As the sun drops behind you, houses start to twinkle. The panorama fizzes with lights switched on by people arriving home from school, work, shopping, bingo, bookies.

The pattern grows more complex as buses weave through the scheme, each leaving in its wake a trail of new lights as disembarking passengers step through their front doors. A trained observer might deduce the rate at which the bus empties on its way to the terminus, and from that chart the city's biorhythms. As they open and close, offices and schools, building sites and health centres, pubs and restaurants, swimming pools and libraries, shopping centres and museums, foodbanks, churches, and cinemas send overlapping ripples of light and darkness out across the scheme.

As lights hop back and forth between different rooms, movement within each home can be observed, and patterns of domestic life inferred. Thus, data can be collated regarding single versus multiple occupancy, eating routines, bathroom habits, quality of sleep. Given sufficient observation time, judgments can be made about residents' well-being: medical disorders, levels of stress, the health of relationships, the need for counselling or intervention.

As [——]'s lights wink through the night, statistical analysis might suggest the local rate of unemployment, the incidence of mental illness, levels of obesity or childhood asthma, the prevalence of sexual dysfunction, percentage of pet ownership, mean disposable income.

Sitting up here watching life surge and recede in the blackness is hypnotic: you lose your sense of scale. Instead of observing thousands of people living out their lives, you might be watching a great bank of blinking LED indicators on a UNIVAC computer array programmed to divine optimum living arrangements in the perfect scheme.

But on the other side of each window, lit or dark, life is lived in analogue, complexity encrypting its essence, keeping secrets beyond the grasp of number crunchers who assume lofty positions but see only dancing lights.

As you descend the hill, you notice that each individual light has its own pulse, fluctuating in intensity: wall-mounted TV screens flash action scenes, dimmer switches subtly alter the mood, teenagers fire green laser beams into the sky.

Schemes of The Past (5)

[——] is a scheme of bings.

From up on the approach road, it looks like a collection of dolls' houses laid out in a field full of molehills.

The impression is reinforced down at street level by the scheme's prim semis with their over-dressed windows, all pelmets and frilly nets, sitting at awkward angles in the gaps between overbearing pit bings.

From the lie of the land, it's clear that the bings, weathered slagheaps covered in scruffy vegetation, were here first. The road wends its way around these mini mountains like a burn wandering through a great glen. Local drivers, ever mindful of the scheme's countless chicanes and treacherous blind spots, move with care and respect for the fluid landscape.

Each bing has a name. This might refer to a physical characteristic – a double hump halfway up its back, a tree at the summit, a dramatic view from its ridge – or it might tell the story of an incident that took place on the bing. Some of these events predate the scheme, and others occurred after it was built.

Residents give the bing's name as the top line of their address and, when introducing themselves, will tell you not only their own name but also the name of their bing. This comes naturally because every local child is taught from birth to think of their bing as their guardian.

If you're brought up here, your bing is always close: standing watch when you peek from your bedroom window after a fevered nightmare, offering a shortcut to the clouds on a spring walk with your first love, a soft presence in your damp eyes when you've lost someone.

But something else binds the people to their bings. At dusk, the huge forms throw shadows on the houses beneath them. Battered by westerlies, they're worn down on one side so, in the fading light, they seem stooped and round shouldered, like old folk readying themselves to shuffle off into the night.

When bedrooms go dark, the bings glide through dreams. They talk to each other, recalling the dolls' houses, reciting the names of everyone who lived here.

Schemes of Coercion (5)

[——] is a scheme of shame.

It lies in a part of the city better known for millionaires' mansions, an area that oozes grandeur, where lampposts are embellished with fronds, iron railings top sandstone walls, demure boulevards give way to dashing avenues, and dappled pavements stretch under green canopies.

Mock baronial castles and Georgian mansions meet driveways that meander past rock gardens, water features, and arched follies. By night, parapets, porticos, balconies, and balustrades throw extravagant shadows over uplit facades.

But these creative flourishes are strictly regulated. As other parts of the city know only too well, brute innovation can be destructive. This area, however, is a World Heritage Site, a source of much local pride, so the slightest alteration is subject to a gruelling planning process under the watch of its ever-vigilant protectors.

It took a war to blow a hole in the conservationists' shield, with planning restrictions temporarily relaxed amid a city-wide housing crisis. Two adjoining plots at the suburb's heart, which had lain undeveloped because no-one could get permission to do anything with them, were snapped up by the council, and within weeks [——], a scheme of temporary prefab huts, was complete.

The new dwellings proved popular with their tenants, though less so with the neighbours. Dubbed 'Tintown', the development immediately caused friction on all sides.

Meetings were held in drawing rooms, and letters written expressing outrage. But while fire fell from the skies, the council's focus remained elsewhere so, to save the city's shining suburb, local action was required.

This particular war effort would exact a high price: some sight lines would be compromised; but still, something had to be done, so it was decided to plant a wall of foliage around the scheme. Yet this front line would be no mere Ardennes. Trees, shrubs, and bushes were selected for fast growth, sharp thorns, and potent stings.

As an impenetrable barrier rose on all sides, Tintown's residents complained, but the council had no wish to further antagonise its top band ratepayers, so the issue was classed as a neighbourly dispute, best left to those involved. Besides, the planters pointed out, with full planning restrictions by now back in force, not a single leaf could be clipped.

As the scheme was slowly strangled by thickening vines, its voice quietened, until the sun was blocked out and its corrugated roofs swallowed up. Now it's impossible to see the scheme from the ground or the air; even on Google Earth it just looks like an overgrown corner of an adjoining garden. No-one has made it in or out for years – get too close and the gorse tears at your clothes, twigs scratch your eyes, epiphytes grab your ankles.

Is the scheme even still there? No-one really knows. The rent still gets paid each month, so the council lets things be. Some say wealthy locals keep the payments going to prevent further investigation. The tenants might still be thriving, happily sealed off from a warring, judgmental world, or maybe they all slipped out in the night after a storm made a temporary clearing in their jungle prison.

In Tintown, [——], anything could be true, but everyone is too ashamed to look.

Schemes of Transport (5)

[——] is a scheme of terminus.

It lies miles from the city centre. To reach it, the bus heads out along a dual carriageway beside a slip road built over an old swing park, then passes beneath a flyover holding up the city's twelve-lane ring road.

Beyond this colossal landmark, the bus skirts a street of flattened tenements from which men once poured into muddy trenches in a far-off land, then speeds through the ghost of an old toll booth, before pulling up briefly at the front step of a vanished maternity hospital that made way for offices, now vacant and burnt out.

The bus moves again, and the windows are slapped by the waving branches of trees that grew on the site of an old cinema, then its wheels plunge into a two-hundred-year-old puddle made by freedom fighters who partially dynamited the aqueduct overhead.

On the other side of the tunnel, the bus emerges beneath a ruined cliff top castle that was once a school for wayward boys, roars past a factory that was worked by the blind, a tanning salon in an old Co-Op building, and skirts a flat expanse on which furnaces once conjured up marvels for Maharajas' palaces.

Straining through the gears, the bus climbs over a rubbish-filled canyon along which laden trains thundered in the night, then, skirting the walls of a disused quarry, crawls round a hairpin bend, its tyres inches from the bricks of ruined cottages lying among the nettles on the verge.

There is no other road to [——], so passing through all these points is the only way to arrive at the scheme's terminus, which is the end point of all the journeys made in this direction.

Schemes of Abandonment (5)

[——] is a scheme of bonfires.

At the edge of the city, a stack of black smoke totters in the sky. As you pass through its shadow, the air chills. You breathe it in: it's more acrid than Shanghai smog, more beguiling than Delhi after dark.

The scheme is a patchwork of open grassland, half-razed streets, and red ash playing fields. Charred discs dot the landscape, some still smouldering. Dogs sniff around the ashes and small children rake the rubble with sticks, seeking treasure.

An eternal flame burns here. It might have been born with the scheme in a workman's brazier, or perhaps local youngsters got it going on the first Guy Fawkes night, or maybe it began as an electrical fire in the high flats, or shot from a furnace in the local forge, or was carried down from a hilltop beacon that told a dozen glens their time had come.

Whatever its origin, the residents feed its beseeching tongues. From a nearby industrial estate, lines of people come and go like ants, straining under pallets, boards, and boxes. The scheme's marshy hinterland is combed for the last striplings of gorse lying low in the stubble.

Gardens were long ago stripped of fences, sheds, dookits, benches; tenements earmarked for demolition were ransacked before the bulldozers came. The scheme will soon be a hollow shell, its remaining houses given to the flames: doors, skirtings, dining tables, bed frames, bookcases, meter boxes, bath panelling—

As night encircles the scheme, people crowd in, and the heat intensifies. Running on ever less efficient fuel, the fire sputters, reddens, and coughs out showers of sparks that drift then lurch in the updraught, throwing themselves against the blackness.

Faces look different around the bonfire: features are sharpened by shadow; eyes burn to see the flames take shape. You realise that [——] is a scheme of sculptors, their medium lighter than air, their fleeting creations not afforded the luxuries of mass, time, rest.

A surge of dry heat catches your throat, driving you back; smoke stings your eyes, forcing you further away. As you leave its circle of warmth, you turn for one last look at the bonfire – a blue-green aurora writhes over the scheme like a tortured genie with no more wishes to grant.

When you return to the city centre, everything seems dull, slow, dead. Lumps of cold iron guard the main square, vigilant against change that has already happened. Meanwhile, on the horizon, a heat haze dances, obscuring the restless hills beyond.

Mark ducks under the twisted police tape and steps up to the reinforced steel door. He takes the key from his pocket and stabs it into the hole; at the first touch, the door dislodges from its frame. With a yelp, Mark dances backwards as it clatters to the ground. He takes a breath, steps over it, and enters.

He reaches for the light switch, then remembers they're all blown out. For the first time, the air smells clean: clear of dust and the vapours of decay. He fumbles for his phone and sweeps it across the blackness, firing out a beam of light.

The whitewashed walls are charred in places, and the floor is carpeted by shredded cardboard, in places a couple of feet deep. He kicks his way through it, clearing a path towards McCann's desk.

He finds it under the debris, lying on its side, and drags it upright. It wobbles on loose legs, but stays standing. He flips up McCann's chair and sits. The light blinks off and darkness rushes him with the force of a searing flash: he visualises the spark arcing from an old cable in the rafters, feeling out across the damp air, converting static electricity and motes of dust to heat and light, setting off a cascade of explosive energy across the unit – the official explanation.

Twisting his neck, he looks up for a slither of sky. The hole is much bigger now; an entire section of the roof is missing. Maybe the flash came from up there, taking McCann out first. But who? An impatient creditor? One of his own men? A name in the notebook? Or maybe he took himself out – or didn't. Maybe the whole thing was staged to make him invisible. Mark runs his palms over the desk, feeling its hammer-shaped indentations scratch at his skin. For a moment, he thinks he can smell a hint of Lacoste aftershave.

The chill of night closes in. He stands, taps his light on and goosesteps across the litter, towards the wall. He gropes for a loose brick, then slowly works it out. Behind it, there's an envelope:

FAO THE INVISIBLE BOY

It contains a notebook, with sections titled 'Politics', 'Football', 'Celebrity', 'Media', 'Law', 'Accountancy', 'CID'; each is crammed with names and swarms of numbers.

'Av read that story Big Man, it ony gets ye so for,' Mark says, stuffing the book back into the hole. He shakes the envelope, and a bank card falls into his open hand. By the light of his phone, its silver embossed letters hover in the dark:

MR MARK MILTON

'I am become a name.'

He slips the card into his pocket, wedges the brick back into place and takes a last look around the unit. His narrow beam of light reaches out across empty space; suddenly the darkness frightens him.

Back outside, he stops at the end of the alley and looks down at his shoes: the earth is at peace. The hills' long shadows enfold the land between them, the Giant's sleep untroubled by morning's first gentle nudge. Mark stands watch as the cover of darkness slips from his face and body; as night dies, shadow and form wrestle for possession of the land.

'What schemes will you dream up next?' Mark asks, walking into the new day.

Acknowledgements

Thank you to everyone at Arkbound Publishers for getting behind this book, particularly, for her enthusiasm, patience and expertise, my editor, Elsie Elder. (Any remaining errors are owned entirely by the author!)

I'd also like to thank the Clutha Trust and its 'Power Over Poverty' campaign for supporting the book, and in particular, for his assistance on many fronts, Alan Crossan.

Thanks also to all my friends who have supported my written efforts over the years, including, for his time and advice on this project, Willy Maley, and above all to my friend Paula Khan, without whose encouragement and support this book wouldn't have come together.